WHSmith

Practice

Maths and English

BUMPER BOOK

**Age 9–11
Years 5–6**
Key Stage 2

Acknowledgements

The publishers would like to thank the following for permission to reproduce copyright material:

p.14 Allan Ahlberg, 'Things I have been doing lately' from *Heard it in the Playground* (Viking, 1989), copyright © Allan Ahlberg, 1989, reprinted by permission of Penguin Books; **p.16** Gill Lewis, from *Sky Hawk* (OUP, 2011), copyright Gill Lewis 2011, reprinted by permission of Oxford University Press; **p.18** Gill Lewis, Biographical note from author page on www.oup.com/oxed/children, copyright © Oxford University Press, reprinted by permission of Oxford University Press; **p.20** 'Shiny to shop' from *The Oxford Illustrated Junior Thesaurus* (OUP, 1999), copyright Oxford University Press 1999, reprinted by permission of Oxford University Press; **p.46** 'Gary's Garden' by Gary Northfield from *Phoenix comic, 27*, The Phoenix Comic, 29 Beaumont Street, Oxford OX1 2NP, www.thephoenixcomic.co.uk; **p.70** Jan Mark: Review of *The Fire-Eaters* by David Almond from the *Guardian* (27 September 2003), copyright Guardian News & Media Ltd 2003, reproduced by permission of Guardian News & Media; **p.72** David Almond: *The Fire-Eaters* (Hodder Children's Books, 2003).

Every effort has been made to trace all copyright holders, but if any have been inadvertently overlooked the Publishers will be pleased to make the necessary arrangements at the first opportunity. Although every effort has been made to ensure that website addresses are correct at time of going to press, Hodder Education cannot be held responsible for the content of any website mentioned in this book. It is sometimes possible to find a relocated web page by typing in the address of the home page for a website in the URL window of your browser.

Hachette UK's policy is to use papers that are natural, renewable and recyclable products and made from wood grown in sustainable forests. The logging and manufacturing processes are expected to conform to the environmental regulations of the country of origin.

Orders: please contact Bookpoint Ltd, 130 Milton Park, Abingdon, Oxon OX14 4SB. Telephone: (44) 01235 827720. Fax: (44) 01235 400454. Lines are open 9.00a.m.–5.00p.m., Monday to Saturday, with a 24-hour message answering service. Visit our website at www.hoddereducation.co.uk.

© Brenda Stones, Steve Mills and Hilary Koll, Richard Cooper 2013
Teacher's tips © Najoud Ensaff and Matt Koster 2013
First published in 2013 exclusively for WHSmith by
Hodder Education
An Hachette UK Company
50 Victoria Embankment
London EC4Y 0DZ

Impression number   10 9 8 7 6 5
Year   2018

This edition has been updated, 2014, to reflect National Curriculum changes.

Cover illustration by Oxford Designers and Illustrators Ltd
Character illustrations: Beehive Illustration
All other illustrations Fakenham Prepress Solutions, Fakenham, Norfolk NR21 8NN
Typeset in Folio by Fakenham Prepress Solutions, Fakenham, Norfolk NR21 8NN
Printed in Spain

A catalogue record for this title is available from the British Library.

ISBN: 978 1444 188 660

Advice for parents

Maths and English *Practice* bumper book

The books in the *Practice* series are designed to practise and consolidate children's work in school. They are intended for children to complete on their own, but you may like to work with them for the first few pages.

This bumper book provides a selection of titles from the *Practice* range for children aged 9–11. This selection consists of two English titles: *English Practice* and *Writing and Punctuation Practice*; and two Maths titles: *Maths Practice* and *Problem Solving Practice*.

Details for all of the titles in the *Practice* Key Stage 2 series can be found on the inside front cover of this book.

When using this book with your child, the following points will help:

- Don't ask your child to do too much at once. A 'little and often' approach is a good way to start.
- Reward your child with lots of praise and encouragement. These should be enjoyable activities for them.
- Discuss with your child what they have learned and what they can do.
- The '**Get ready**' section provides a gentle warm-up for the topic covered on the page.
- The '**Let's practise**' section is usually the main activity. This section helps to consolidate understanding of the topic.
- The '**Have a go**' section is often a challenge or something interesting that your child can go away and do which is related to the topic. It may require your child to use everyday objects around the home.
- The '**How have I done**?' section at the end of the book is a short informal test that should be attempted when all the units have been completed. It is useful for spotting gaps in knowledge, which can then be revisited at a suitable moment.
- The '**Teacher's tips**' are written by practising classroom teachers. They give useful advice on specific topics or skills, to deepen your child's understanding and confidence and to help you help your child.

Contents

WRITING AND PUNCTUATION

MATHS

PROBLEM SOLVING

Welcome to Kids Club!

Hi, readers. My name's Charlie and I run Kids Club with my friend Abbie. Kids Club is an after-school club which is very similar to one somewhere near you.

We'd love you to come and join our club and see what we get up to!

I'm Abbie. Let's meet the kids who will work with you on the activities in this book.

My name's Jamelia. I look forward to Kids Club every day. The sports and games are my favourites, especially at Kids Camp in the school holidays.

Hi, I'm Megan. I've made friends with all the kids at Kids Club. I like the outings and trips we go on the best.

Hello, my name's Kim. Kids Club is a great place to chill out after school. My best friend is Alfie – he's a bit naughty but he means well!

I'm Amina. I like to do my homework at Kids Club. Charlie and Abbie are always very helpful. We're like one big happy family.

Greetings, readers, my name's Alfie! Everybody knows me here. Come and join our club; we'll have a wicked time together!

Now you've met us all, tell us something about yourself. All the kids filled in a '**Personal profile**' when they joined. Here's one for you to complete.

Personal profile

Name: _____

Age: _____

School: _____

Home town: _____

Best friend: _____

My favourite:

● Book _____,

● Film _____,

● Food _____,

● Sport _____.

My hero is _____ because _____
_____.

When I grow up I want to be a _____.

If I ruled the world the first thing I would do is _____
_____.

If I could be any celebrity for a day I would be _____
_____.

English

- Covers the key knowledge
- Exercises for all the core skills

1: Word reading

It is good to keep increasing the number of words you know: this is called your **vocabulary**.

Get ready

For each of the words that follow:

- say it out loud
- write what it means
- use it in a short sentence.

Let's practise

Ancient means: _____

My sentence: _____

Appreciate means: _____

My sentence: _____

Atmosphere means: _____

My sentence: _____

Committee means: _____

My sentence: _____

Correspond means: _____

My sentence: _____

Curious means: _____

My sentence: _____

Definite means: _____

My sentence: _____

Especially means: _____

My sentence: _____

Genuine means: _____

My sentence: _____

Interrupt means: _____

My sentence: _____

Marvellous means: _____

My sentence: _____

Mosquito means: _____

My sentence: _____

Nuisance means: _____

My sentence: _____

Persevere means: _____

My sentence: _____

Succeed means: _____

My sentence: _____

Suggest means: _____

My sentence: _____

Theatre means: _____

My sentence: _____

Twelfth means: _____

My sentence: _____

Wisdom means: _____

My sentence: _____

Zoology means: _____

My sentence: _____

 **Have a go**

Make a collection of words you like the sound of.
Don't worry about the meaning for now!

Teacher's tips

You'll find using a **dictionary** helpful when you write the **meanings** of these words.
The best thing to do is write the meaning in your own words so that you remember it.
Remember, reading **books** will help you to widen your **vocabulary**.

These two pages are about how to read and enjoy poetry and understand what it means.

 Get ready

There are lots of different ways of reading a poem:

- read it quietly to yourself
- think what kind of poem it is, e.g. rhyming, free verse or narrative
- think about how you would read it out loud, with what kind of expression
- give a performance of the poem to other people
- learn it by heart.

Read this poem by Allan Ahlberg to yourself.

Things I have been doing lately

Things I have been doing lately:
Pretending to go mad
Eating my own cheeks from the inside
Growing taller
Keeping a secret
Keeping a worm in a jar
Keeping a good dream going
Picking a scab on my elbow
Rolling a cat up in a rug
Blowing bubbles in my spit
Making myself dizzy
Holding my breath
Pressing my eyeballs so that I become temporarily blind
Being very nearly ten
Practising my signature...

Saving the best till last.

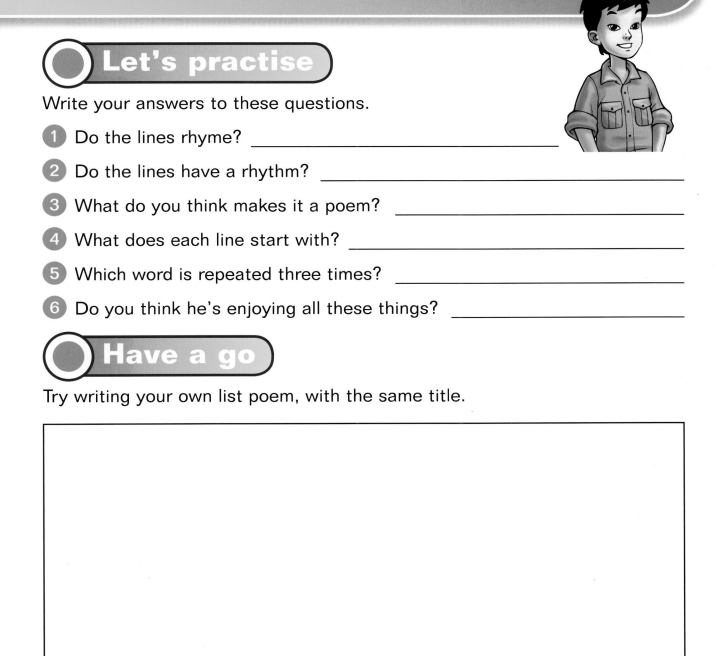

Let's practise

Write your answers to these questions.

1. Do the lines rhyme? _____

2. Do the lines have a rhythm? _____

3. What do you think makes it a poem? _____

4. What does each line start with? _____

5. Which word is repeated three times? _____

6. Do you think he's enjoying all these things? _____

Have a go

Try writing your own list poem, with the same title.

Teacher's tips

The word poem comes from the ancient Greek word *poema* which broadly means 'a making'. Why not read some poems before you write your own? Poets such as **Ken Nesbitt** and **Murray Lachlan Young** will definitely entertain you.

3: Comprehension – fiction

These two pages are about reading and understanding stories.

When we read a story, we need to understand not just what is happening, but also:

- what kind of story it is; e.g. fairy story, science fiction or humour
- who wrote it
- who the characters are, and what their characteristics are
- what the setting of the story is
- what might happen next.

Read this page from *Sky Hawk* by Gill Lewis, about a bird called an osprey.

Iona undid the plastic catches and opened the lid. Inside was a small rectangular black box, a long thin wire, and small harness that looked as if it would fit a toy bear.

'It's a satellite transmitter,' Hamish said. 'Latest technology. We strap it to her back, a bit like a mini rucksack. It tells us her position. You know, where she is in the world. We can tell how high she's flying and how fast. We can follow her journey all the way to Africa and back.'

'Brilliant,' I said.

'Isn't it a bit heavy?' frowned Iona.

'No. Here, feel it.' Hamish handed it to Iona. She held it in her palm and curled her fingers around it.

'But how can *we* find out where she's been?' I asked.

'I'll give you a special code,' he said. 'You put it into your computer and it plots her journey on Google Earth. You might even be able to see which tree she roosts in.'

'So we can actually see her fly?' asked Iona.

'No,' said Hamish. 'Google Earth has satellite pictures of the Earth that were taken before now, but you can see the sort of places she flies over.'

The osprey jabbed at the leather gloves with her beak while Hamish tied the straps of the transmitter.

Write your answers to these questions.

1 How many characters are talking? _____

2 What three things will the transmitter record? _____

_____

3 Will the transmitter hurt the bird? _____

4 How does the bird respond to them? _____

_____

5 What is the word that describes how birds fly to Africa and back?

_____

6 How can you tell this is fiction rather than non-fiction?

_____

7 What is the effect of the dialogue in the text? _____

_____

8 What do you think might happen next? _____

_____

_____

Have a go

Look at the RSPB website for tracking the Loch Garten ospreys.
You can follow real birds' journeys as they fly to Africa.

Teacher's tips

Fiction is a **narrative** (story) that is **invented** or **untrue**. You can probably work out what non-fiction is based on this definition of fiction! Remember, a character is someone in a story.

These two pages are about understanding informational text.

 **Get ready**

When you are reading non-fiction or information, there are different things to look out for:

- the purpose of the information
- the layout of the page
- the use of illustrations to give information
- the different kinds of language used.

This is a short biography of the author who wrote the novel on page 16.

The biography comes from her publisher's website.

○ ○ ○   Internet Browser

◁ ▷   ✕   www.oup.com/oxed/children/authors/lewisg

A   Before she could walk, Gill Lewis was discovered force-feeding bread to a sick hedgehog under the rose bushes.

B   Now her stories reflect her passion for wild animals in wild places.

C   She draws inspiration from many of the people she has had the fortune to meet during her work as a vet, both at home and abroad.

D   Gill Lewis has a Masters Degree in Writing for Young People from Bath Spa University, and won the 2009 course prize for Most Promising Writer.

E   Her first novel was snapped up for publication within hours of being offered to publishers.

F   She lives in Somerset with her young family and a motley crew of pets.

G   She writes from a shed in the garden, in the company of spiders.

 **Let's practise**

Write your answers to these questions.

1. What is the author's great passion? _____

2. What was her first job? _____

3. Has she travelled much? _____

4. What did she study at university? _____

5. Does she have children? _____

6. Why do you think her pets are described with that particular

   phrase? _____

7. Is the biography written in the first person or the third person?

   _____

8. How many times is a pronoun used instead of her name?

   _____

9. Plot which period in time each sentence describes.

Past	Present	Future
A	—	

 **Have a go**

Try rewriting the sentences in a sequence from past to present. Which version do you think works better, and why?

Teacher's tips

Remember, a **biography** is an account of someone else's life. For question 6, look at how her pets are described, then look up any unfamiliar words in a dictionary. For question 9 look out for words that suggest time, and check the verb tenses that are used.

These two pages are about understanding reference books – this time a thesaurus.

 **Get ready**

Reference books are organised in special ways, to make them easy to use.

In the example below:

- the 'headwords' are listed in alphabetical order
- the designer has used bold type and colour to make the headwords stand out
- the word classes are put in italics
- the sentences demonstrate the word in context
- the synonyms, or words with similar meanings, are in bold type.

Look at this text from an illustrated thesaurus:

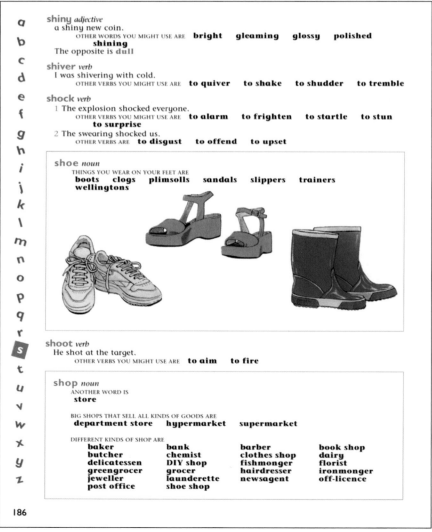

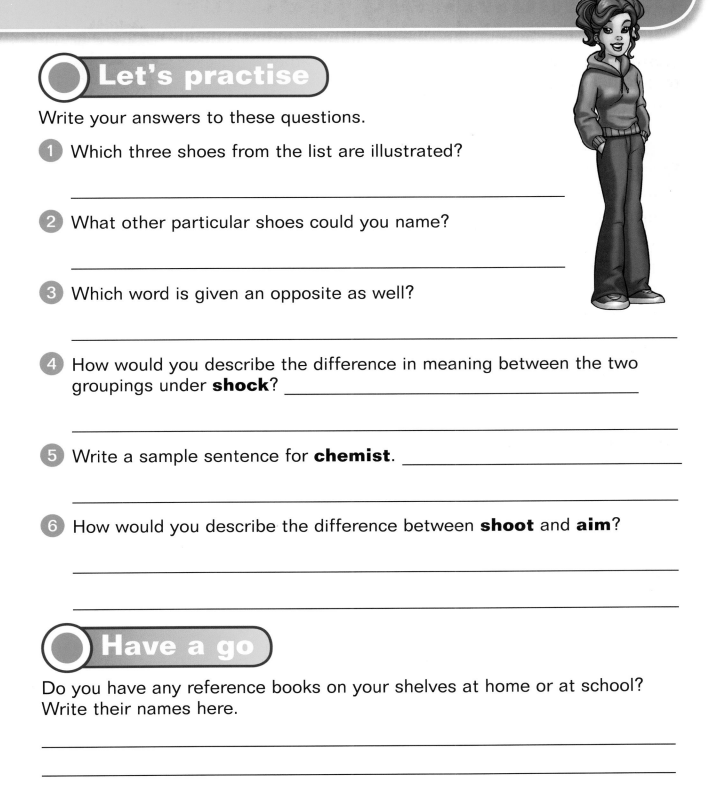

Let's practise

Write your answers to these questions.

1 Which three shoes from the list are illustrated?

_____

2 What other particular shoes could you name?

_____

3 Which word is given an opposite as well?

_____

4 How would you describe the difference in meaning between the two groupings under **shock**? _____

_____

5 Write a sample sentence for **chemist**. _____

_____

6 How would you describe the difference between **shoot** and **aim**?

_____

_____

Have a go

Do you have any reference books on your shelves at home or at school? Write their names here.

_____

_____

_____

Teacher's tips

The term **thesaurus** is derived from the ancient Greek *thesauros* meaning 'storehouse,' or 'treasure'. *The Historical Thesaurus of the Oxford English Dictionary* (HTOED) is the **largest** thesaurus in the world, but there are many others. Have a search online for yourself.

6: Handwriting practice

Sometimes you need to use printed letters rather than joined handwriting.

Using the key, write labels on the diagram in clear printed letters.

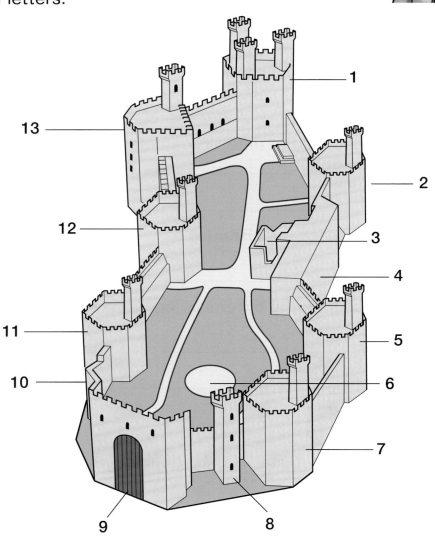

Key

1	Eagle Tower	**8**	Watchtower
2	Well Tower	**9**	Queen's Gate
3	Prison Tower	**10**	Cistern Tower
4	King's Gate	**11**	Black Tower
5	Granary Tower	**12**	Chamberlain Tower
6	Investiture Dais	**13**	Queen's Tower
7	NE Tower		

Let's practise

Now practise some lines of regular handwriting: either all upright strokes, or if they slope then make it a regular slope for all your words.

Copy out the poem from page 14 of this book, and add your own illustrations round the edge.

Teacher's tips

When writing the labels, write each letter separately and clearly. You probably know **regular handwriting** better as **joined-up writing** although another term is **cursive writing.** Remember to write very slowly at first.

7: Spelling – letter strings

One of the trickiest spellings in English is **ough**, because it can be said in so many different ways.

It comes from the old Anglo-Saxon language.

 **Get ready**

The most common form of this spelling is **ought**, which we say as 'ort'.

Here are five very different verbs that all use this spelling in their past form.

Draw lines to match them to their correct past tense.

| buy | bring | fight | seek | think |

ought

thorough

sort

fort

though

thought

bought

fraught

brought

fought

sought

taught

There are actually seven ways of saying the **ough** spelling!

Write each word in the right jar.

cough   through   drought   nought   although
plough   thorough   rough   enough   borough
though   dough   tough   trough

off   oh   oo   ow

or   uh   uff

Have a go

Here are two more awkward spellings. Can you fill in the words and say them out loud?

aught	eight
c_ _ _ _ _	fr_ _ _ _ _
fr_ _ _ _ _	w_ _ _ _ _
d_ _ _ _ _er	sl_ _ _ _ _
h_ _ _ _y	h_ _ _ _ _

Teacher's tips

Write each of the words in **Get ready** on a post-it note and place against each of the five present tense verbs listed ('buy' to 'think'), until the match seems to make sense! You won't use all the words.

8: Spelling – suffixes

There are a lot of words that end with **-able**, like **adorable** and **drinkable**.

But there are just a few words that end with **-ible**, like **possible** and **terrible**.

How do you know which spelling to use?

 **Get ready**

If the suffix is added onto a root verb, the spelling is **-able**.

But remember your spelling rules for suffixes: double the last consonant after a short vowel, and remove the final **e**, except after **ce** or **ge**.

Fill in this grid!

Root verb	Add the suffix
change	changeable
comfort	
consider	
depend	
enjoy	
notice	
reason	
understand	
stop	
like	

These words don't have immediate root verbs, so end **-ible**.

possible   **terrible**   **horrible**   **incredible**   **sensible**

Let's practise

Here are two more tricky suffixes: **-ent** and **-ant**.

It actually depends on what kind of Latin verb the word came from – but here is an easier way to work it out:

- Nouns with an **a** in their suffix turn into adjectives with an **a**.
- Nouns with an **e** in their suffix turn into adjectives with an **e**.

Fill in the gaps!

Noun	Adjective
expect**a**tion	expectant
hesit**a**tion	
observ**a**tion	
confid**e**nce	confident
independ**e**nce	
obedi**e**nce	

Have a go

One exception is **dependent** and **dependant**, both correct, but which is which?

_____

_____

_____

Check your dictionary for the answer!

Teacher's tips

Why not keep a file of all the spelling rules? You could write the **-able** spelling rule on a piece of card which you laminate and place in this file. In addition to **-able, -ible, -ent,** and **-ant**, there are many other suffixes, such as **-ous**, **-some** and **-al**. Why not have a look at some of these, too?

9: Spelling – homophones

Homophones are words that sound the same but are spelt differently.

Often there are ways to remember which spelling is which.

 Get ready

Read the words that sound the same below, then choose the correct spellings on the next page.

princip**le** – noun	princip**al** – adjective
pract**ice** – noun	pract**ise** – verb
licen**ce** – noun	licen**se** – verb
effect – usually a noun	**a**ffect – usually a verb
past – noun, adjective, preposition, adverb	passed – verb
station**ar**y, for **car**s	station**er**y, for pap**er**s
compl**i**ment, be n**i**ce	compl**e**ment, make compl**e**te
de**s**ert, an arid place	de**ss**ert, pudding with double helpings
al**ta**r, a **ta**ble in a church	alter, to change
a**loud**, out **loud**	a**ll**owed, permi**tt**ed
led, past form of lead	le**a**d gives you **a**sthma

Let's practise

1. The _____ thing is to remember the _____. (principal/principle)

2. I must _____ how to do my _____. (practise/practice)

3. My driving _____ _____s me to drive a car. (licence/license)

4. I'm not sure how that will _____ me; there could be a big _____. (affect/effect)

5. I _____ by and then hurried on _____. (past/passed)

6. My car is _____ while I buy some _____. (stationery/stationary)

7. Give me a _____; it will _____ the others I've received. (compliment/complement)

8. We stagger across the _____ to reach a place that serves _____. (desert/dessert)

9. We pray at the _____; hoping that will _____ things for us. (altar/alter)

10. Is it _____ to call _____? (aloud/allowed)

Have a go

Now try writing two sentences to show the different meanings of **led/lead**.

_____

_____

10: Spelling – common errors

The pairs of words on this page have such different meanings that you just need to learn their different spellings.

Get ready

Choose and copy the right word for **a** and **b** of each pair.

1. (aisle/isle)
   Which is a small island?   Which is a gangway?
   a _____   **b** _____

2. (farther/father)
   Which one has sons and
   daughters?   Which one is beyond?
   a _____   **b** _____

3. (guessed/guest)
   Which is someone who   Which is the past tense of
   comes to stay?   **guess**?
   a _____   **b** _____

4. (herd/heard)
   Which is a group of animals?   Which is the past tense of **hear**?
   a _____   **b** _____

5. (serial/cereal)
   Which do you eat for   Which is a run of TV
   breakfast?   programmes?
   a _____   **b** _____

6. (draught/draft)
   Which is a gust of air?   Which is a first version?
   a _____   **b** _____

7. (steal/steel)
   Which is a metal?   Which means to rob?
   a _____   **b** _____

8. (bridle/bridal)
   Which is about weddings?   Which is about horses?
   a _____   **b** _____

9. (prophet/profit)
   Which is about money?   Which is about religion?
   a _____   **b** _____

10. (morning/mourning)
    Which happens after death?   Which happens early in the day?
    a _____   **b** _____

Let's practise

Sometimes it helps to split tricky words into their prefix, root word and suffix.

Here's an example. See how many words you can make with these building blocks.

ad		ed
com		ing
e		
o		
per	mit	
re		
sub		ssion
trans		

There should be a total of 8 × 4 = 32.

Remember that you'll have to change the spelling when you add a suffix.

Then check the meaning of each word you've created!

Have a go

Invent a misunderstanding over one of the pairs of words on page 30. It could happen in a conversation between two people.

Write it here.

Teacher's tips

For the questions on page 30, you can use a dictionary (online or book) to find the definition of each word. For the questions on this page, remember when you add the **suffixes -ing**, **-ed** and **-ssion** you will need to watch your spelling.

11: Grammar – active and passive

An active verb looks like this: I <u>sent</u> the letter.
A passive verb looks like this: The letter <u>was sent</u> by me.

With an active verb, the subject (**I**) usually comes first.
With a passive verb, the object (**the letter**) usually comes first.

 **Get ready**

Rewrite these sentences in the passive; notice which other words you have to change.

1 He sent the email last week.

_____

2 She sent a reply immediately.

_____

3 The message really caught her attention.

_____

4 He sent another email the next morning.

_____

5 She rang him to discuss it further.

_____

6 He dropped his phone in surprise.

_____

7 She told her friends all about it.

_____

8 They passed the message on.

_____

9 Nobody could answer the question.

_____

Let's practise

Now change these sentences from passive to active.
Again, notice which words you have to change apart from the verb.

1 The insect was studied by the scientist.

_____

2 Its diet was also observed for a week.

_____

3 The scientist's results were recorded in the newspaper.

_____

4 The newspaper's sales were raised that week.

_____

5 This was unexpected by everybody.

_____

6 The scientist was praised by everybody.

_____

7 The insect was forgotten soon after.

_____

Have a go

What have you learnt about the difference between active and passive sentences?

When do you think passive sentences are better to use than active sentences?

Teacher's tips

Remember, in the **active voice**, the subject actively performs the action. In the **passive voice**, the subject receives the action. It's _usually_ better to use the active voice, but not always!

Remember that a clause is a part of a sentence that includes a verb, and a sentence can be built with several clauses.

A clause that starts with **who**, **which**, **where**, **when** or **whose** is called a **relative clause**.

Get ready

Write a relative clause for each of these sentences.

1 The monster, who _____, had bright red spots.

2 The monster scratched his spots, which _____.

3 The monster, whose _____, griped and groaned.

4 The garden shed, where _____, began to shake.

5 The monster's friend was the gardener, who _____.

6 The gardener's boots, which _____, had scarlet laces.

7 I often hid in the shed, where _____.

8 The best time is at night, when _____.

Now underline each verb in your relative clauses and in the main sentences.

What did you notice about the position of the relative clause in the sentences? And what did you notice about the punctuation around the relative clause?

Let's practise

Add relative clauses to these sentences, thinking about the position and the punctuation.

Use each of these linking words at least once:
who, **which**, **where**, **when**, **whose**.

1 Monsters often live in garden sheds.

_____

2 They like sheds on dry soil.

_____

3 They like a warm and sunny climate.

_____

4 Monsters usually come out at night.

_____

5 The boots belonged to the gardener.

_____

6 The laces belonged to the boots.

_____

7 Monsters don't eat laces.

_____

8 Monsters don't eat gardeners.

_____

Again, underline each verb in both clauses.

Write a sentence of advice to a friend on how to add relative clauses.

_____

Teacher's tips

An example of a sentence with a relative clause is: 'The man, who lived at number 37, left early every day.' A **relative clause** is one type of **subordinate clause**. It does not make sense on its own! The part of the sentence 'The man left early every day' is a **main clause** and it makes sense on its own.

13: Punctuation – brackets and dashes

In the last unit, you used commas to separate a relative clause, which was an 'aside' from the main sentence.

We shall now look at how you can use brackets for a more closed-off aside, and dashes for a more informal aside.

 **Get ready**

Write asides in brackets to add to these sentences.

1 The king (...) gave up his throne.

_____

2 The queen (...) followed him.

_____

3 The public (...) were very upset.

_____

4 The press had a field day (...).

_____

5 History will make up its own mind (...).

_____

6 I'll give you my opinion later (...).

_____

Now check on two things:

- Did you use verbs within brackets? (It's all right to do so!)
- Where did you put any punctuation at the end of the brackets? (1 to 3 must not have commas after the brackets; but 4 to 6 must have a full stop outside the final bracket.)

Now try using dashes for adding an aside. The key thing is to remember to use two dashes if they're in the middle of a sentence. But you might use just one dash – for a kind of afterthought.

1. I discovered this old house – _____ – down by the coast.

2. It had the spookiest rooms – _____ – upstairs.

3. Round the windows – _____ – was trailing ivy.

4. I went up the drive – _____ .

5. I thought I saw someone – _____ .

6. Maybe it was just the wind – _____ .

Have a go

Now write some punctuation rules for writing asides.

- brackets: _____
  _____

- dashes: _____
  _____

- commas: _____
  _____

Teacher's tips

Words contained in **brackets** (parentheses) or between or after **dashes** add information which could be removed without the sentence losing sense. For example, 'The queen (who recently arrived) is visiting today – at 4 p.m.' Don't confuse hyphens (to break up one word, or separate two) with dashes.

14: Punctuation – semicolons and colons

There are two very useful punctuation marks that will help you break up your sentences in different ways: the semicolon (;) and the colon (:).

 **Get ready**

The semicolon, or half colon, balances equal parts of a sentence:

Half of him wanted to go; half of him wanted to stay.
In the morning it rains; in the afternoon it rains harder.

Write second halves for these sentences.

1. The queen wears a crown; the king _____

2. Film stars have big houses; football stars _____

    _____

3. Boys make a noise; whereas girls _____

4. Last year's holidays were a wash-out; whereas next year's

    holidays _____

5. Reading is fun; writing is _____

6. I like chocolate; my friend _____

7. Dogs show their feelings; cats _____

8. I know what I want; you _____

Let's practise

The colon is different: it sends the sense forward into the second part of the sentence.

It can also be used before a list, and so there doesn't have to be a verb following a colon.

Write second halves for these sentences.

1. This was his shopping list: apples, _____

2. Here's my choice of pudding: _____

3. There are just two things I want for my birthday: _____

_____

4. Our school stands out: _____

5. When I look in the mirror I see: _____

6. I'm going to be different: _____

7. Here's my plan for next week: _____

8. Breakfast will be the usual: _____

Have a go

Now decide which of these sentences need colons and which need semicolons:

1. This week is nearly done_____ the next has not yet begun.

2. Here's my plan for next week_____ fun, fun, fun.

3. I can't wait till next week_____ that's when we go away.

4. Holidays first_____ work after.

Teacher's tips

Semi-colons separate two closely related sentences/main clauses. **Colons** can introduce a list or separate two main clauses/sentences where the second is an explanation of the first. For example: 'She entered the room; there was no-one in there', compared with 'She was scared: the room was dark'.

Before you start writing a long piece of **fiction**, you need to spend time planning.

What do you need to plan for fiction?

Get ready

Think about:

- the genre of story (e.g. fantasy or reality)
- the theme of the story (e.g. bullying or escape)
- the setting, the characters, the plot
- the beginning, the middle and the end.

Let's practise

Look back to the story about the osprey on page 16.

Could you write about some kind of wildlife? If you don't know enough facts about the animals you could make it up, as this is fiction.

Plan your story, using the boxes below.

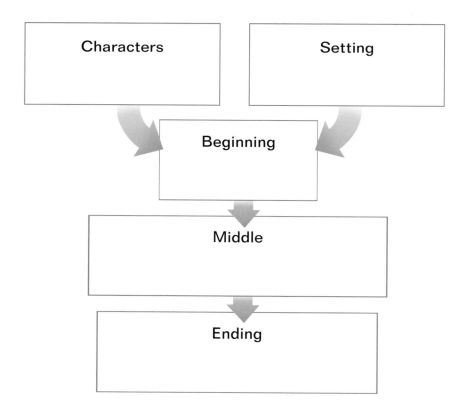

Before you start writing a piece of **non-fiction**, you need to plan rather different things.

What do you need to plan for non-fiction?

 **Get ready**

Think about:

- the audience (who's going to read it)
- the purpose (what you want to achieve)
- the format (printed or online; a flier, or in a journal ...)
- planning your paragraphs
- planning the style of language.

 **Let's practise**

Look back at the short biography on page 18.

Think of someone else whose life you'd like to describe. They could be well-known, or someone just known to you.

Make notes under the headings below, ready for page 44.

Format: is it going to be on a website, or the back of a book, or somewhere else?

_____

Purpose: why will people want to read it?

_____

Audience: what kind of people will want to read it?

_____

Structure: will it be in date order, or not?

_____

Style: will it be simple and factual, or humorous?

_____

Teacher's tips

People plan in different ways. You can make a list of points or create a mind-map of your ideas. Read examples of narratives or stories and biographies to help you decide what to include and how to write.

16: Composition – narrative

Using your planning from page 40, you should be ready to write your story.

Using your planning from page 40

Get ready

You could try telling the story out loud to somebody. Or try writing out a couple of sentences, to help you decide on the style and the point of view.

Let's practise

When you're ready, get started writing the story!

Beginning

Middle

Ending

Now for the final stages of writing your narrative.

First, go back and edit the spellings, punctuation or anything you'd like to change.

Then, evaluate what you've written: how good is it?

You could read it aloud to somebody else, and see what they think of it.

When you're completely happy with it, you could copy it out as a final version.

Teacher's tips

Usually, the middle section of story is where all the action is. Stories need **drama** to get moving. Introduce a complication or problem that characters have to overcome in your middle section.

Using your planning from page 41, you should be ready to write your biography.

 **Get ready**

Check through the notes you made under the different headings.

Have you got a photo of the person you could use?

Have you planned out the sequence of sentences?

Try writing a rough version in the box below.

Teacher's tips

Paragraphing is important in any kind of writing. Remember to start a new paragraph whenever you introduce a new subject in your piece of writing. Practice makes perfect, so the more you write the better you will get at it.

Review your rough version, and decide what could be improved.

Now write a final version here, and maybe design or decorate around it too.

Have a go

Now it's time to evaluate again.

Show it to other people to see what they think.

Decide what you could do better next time.

All writers have to draft and redraft many times!

18: Composition – dialogue

Dialogue is another word for speech, or what people say.

Remember, there are several ways of laying out speech when you're writing:

- speech bubbles
- playscripts
- direct speech.

 **Get ready**

Read this part of a story called 'Gary's Garden' from the new *Phoenix* comic.

thephoenixcomic.co.uk

Teacher's tips

When you write in **direct speech**, remember to take a new line every time a different person speaks. Also, as well as using 'said', liven up your writing with words like 'screeched', 'yelled', 'whispered', 'mumbled' and so on.

Turn the dialogue into a playscript between the three birds of the 'chorus'.

You could invent names for the birds, or just call them 1, 2 and 3.

When you're not sure who's speaking, you can just say 'Voices off' as a stage direction.

_____ : _____

_____ : _____

_____ : _____

Voices off : _____

_____ : _____

_____ : _____

_____ : _____

Voices off : _____

 **Have a go**

Now turn the same dialogue into direct speech, with speech marks, in a narrative.

You'll find it takes more space to explain what's happening between the speeches.

_____

_____

_____

_____

_____

_____

_____

_____

_____

How have I done?

Comprehension

List some distinctive features for each of these genres of text.

Poetry: _____

_____

Fiction: _____

_____

Information: _____

_____

Reference: _____

_____

Handwriting

When do you use print? _____

When do you use joins? _____

And what kind of script might you use for your own notes?

_____

Spelling

List three words with **ough** spellings but different sounds:

_____

List three words with suffix **-able**:

_____

List three words with suffix **-ible**:

_____

List three words with suffix **-ant**:

_____

List three words with suffix **-ent**:

_____

Grammar

Write one sentence with an active verb and an object:

_____

_____

Now write the same sentence in the passive:

_____

_____

Now add a relative clause to the sentence:

_____

_____

_____

Punctuation

Take your active sentence above and add an aside in brackets:

_____

_____

Take the same sentence and add a more informal aside with dashes:

_____

_____

Composition

Punctuate this piece of dialogue:

The quick brown fox was exhausted Not more jumping he said
Well said the lazy dog you dont want to lose your reputation do you
Oh well just this time the fox moaned and changed into his trainers

_____

_____

_____

_____

_____

Writing and Punctuation

- Exercises to build skills
- Write well and be understood

1: Write a poem

Do you know what a **limerick** is? It's usually a funny poem, which follows the pattern of lines and rhymes of the examples below.

One poet who wrote a lot of limericks was Edward Lear. His first book of 'nonsense verse' came out in 1846. Here are two of his limericks.

There was an old person of Dean,
Who dined on one pea and one bean;
    For he said, "More than that
    Would make me too fat,"
That cautious old person of Dean.

There was an old person in grey,
Whose feelings were tinged with dismay;
    She purchased two parrots,
    And fed them with carrots,
Which pleased that old person in grey.

Get ready

1 How many lines do limericks have? _____

2 How many syllables do they have in each line? _____

3 Which lines rhyme? _____

4 In which lines are phrases repeated? _____

Let's practise

Now you try writing a limerick.

You could make it start:
'There was a young girl/boy . . .'

Make sure you follow the lines and
the rhyme patterns opposite.

_____

_____

_____

_____

_____

Have a go

Search for limericks on the Internet.
Which are the funniest you find?
Do they all follow the same pattern?

Teacher's tips

Read the limerick aloud and beat out the syllables on a table. This will help you to
remember the rhythm, which will be useful for when you write your own limerick.

2: Write a playscript

Do you ever spend time listening to what people really say in conversation?

To write a scene for a play, you need to separate what people say (the **speech**) from what they do (the **stage directions**).

Read this example, looking at what's in the speech and what's in the stage directions or actions.

[*The family are seated round the table.* AUNT FORD *is serving roast lamb to her nephews.*]
AUNT FORD: Sam, would you like some roast lamb, with potatoes and caper sauce?
SAM: Yes please, Aunt.
[AUNT FORD *gives him a good portion, and he wolfs it down.*]

AUNT FORD: Would you like some more, Sam?
SAM: Yes, please. I'd like a huge helping, a monster helping, a ginormous helping, please!
MUM: Careful, Sam!
[SAM *finishes this portion as well.*]

AUNT FORD: Sam, could you eat another helping?
MUM: Sam, you know that enough is as good as a feast.
SAM: No, I think that *too much* is the only thing that's as good as a feast!
[SAM *starts to eat, but begins to look a bit ill as he keeps eating . . .*]

 **Get ready**

1. How are the stage directions written? _____

2. What tense are they written in? _____

3. How are the characters' names written? _____

4. Are there any speech marks in playscripts? _____

5. What makes the plot move forward, the speech or the stage directions?
_____

Write a part of a playscript.

You could start by listening to what people say on the bus, or in a TV drama or soap.

Then decide what goes in the speech, and what goes in the stage directions.

_____

_____

_____

_____

_____

_____

_____

 **Have a go**

Try recording a bit of conversation at home and then write it down.
Lay it out as in the example opposite.

Teacher's tips

Look at the type of font used in the stage directions and speech when you answer question 1 and question 3. For question 5 think about what creates most drama.

There are other ways we could write the speeches from the playscript in Unit 2.

If we turned them into **direct speech** in a story, they'd read like this:

"Sam, would you like some roast lamb, with potatoes and caper sauce?" asked Aunt Ford.

"Yes please, Aunt," he replied.

She served him a good portion, and he wolfed it down.

She then asked, "Would you like some more, Sam?"

"Yes, please," he said. "I'd like a huge helping, a monster helping, a ginormous helping, please!"

Mum began to get anxious: "Careful, Sam!"

But Sam finished that portion as well.

When Aunt Ford asked, "Sam, could you eat another helping?" Mum got really anxious.

"Sam, you know that enough is as good as a feast."

But Sam's answer was, "No, I think that *too much* is the only thing that's as good as a feast!"

Get ready

1 What punctuation has been added? _____

2 Does the punctuation at the end of each speech go inside or outside the speech marks? _____

3 When do you start a new line? _____

4 What different verbs are used instead of 'said'? _____

Let's practise

Another way of writing speech is **reported speech**. This means that you relate what was said, but not in speech marks.

Look at the example below, where I have started to write out the dialogue opposite in reported speech. Continue writing the rest of the passage in the same way. You will need to use a separate piece of paper to complete the passage.

Aunt Ford asked Sam whether he'd like some roast lamb, with potatoes and caper sauce.

He said eagerly that he would . . . _____

_____

_____

_____

_____

_____

_____

Have a go

Write a whole conversation in three forms: as a playscript, as direct speech and as reported speech. Which version works best, do you feel? Why?

Teacher's tips

Unlike direct speech, reported speech has no actual words written in speech marks. Make sure your *Let's practice* section has no speech marks or actual spoken words!

4: Plan and write a story

Have you used this 'Y plan' before, for planning a story?

It helps you think through the characters and the setting, before you get on to the beginning, middle and ending of the plot.

Characters	Setting
The merchant and his wife	Holland, a few centuries ago, when people grew prize tulip bulbs

Beginning
The merchant develops a prize-winning bulb.

Middle
The merchant's wife goes out to the kitchen to prepare dinner.

Ending
What does the merchant discover?

1 What do you predict might happen from this plan?

_____

2 In particular, what might happen when the merchant's wife goes to prepare dinner? _____

Let's practise

Write out your own version of the story in Megan's plan.

Give your story at least three paragraphs, one each for the beginning, the middle and the ending. Start here with a paragraph or two as an introduction, to describe the setting and the characters. You may need to continue on a separate piece of paper.

Have a go

Research more about this period in Holland, when tulip bulbs were so valuable. See if you can find the names of some famous Dutch artists of the time.

Teacher's tips

Think carefully about what would make the ending interesting. Remember, if this is set many years ago there won't be TVs, mobile phones, buses, computers and so on.

Here's our version of the whole story, from the plan in Unit 4.

There was once a merchant and his wife, who lived in Holland many centuries ago. This was the time when tulip bulbs were terribly valuable, because everyone wanted to see different kinds of tulips: plain colours, patterned colours, stripes and fluted petals. The best tulips used to raise thousands of gilders!

This merchant was especially good at growing tulips. He was breeding the bulbs, and developing the best colour combinations in the whole of Holland. He kept them in the dark under the stairs, but occasionally brought them out when he was ready to put them in for prizes. And this was what he did one winter's evening, when he was getting ready for the biggest awards of the year.

That evening the merchant's wife was in a hurry to prepare dinner, as she was going out to lace-making classes as soon as she'd done the washing up. So she didn't even bother to light the lamp in the kitchen, but just chopped up all the ingredients for a stew and put it on to simmer.

Just imagine what the merchant felt when he went into the kitchen after his wife had gone out, and searched for the prize bulb he'd put out ready. Just imagine his language when he found the onion peelings in the bin. No, they weren't onion peelings, it was the skin of his prize tulip bulb, skulking at the bottom of the bin with all the leftovers from dinner . . .

Get ready

1 Is this what you expected from the plan?

_____

2 How does it compare with your version of the story?

_____

3 Which bits are better or worse than yours?

_____

Let's practise

Let's imagine a more cheerful ending to the story. Let's imagine that something different happened when the merchant's wife went out to the kitchen.

Write an **alternative** ending to the story, one that leaves the merchant able to enter his prize bulb for the Top Tulip Awards.

_____

_____

_____

_____

_____

_____

_____

_____

Have a go

Think of a traditional story that has a sad ending, like the Pied Piper of Hamelin. Rewrite the story with a happy ending. Which version works better? Why?

Teacher's tips

If you don't feel confident using or punctuating speech marks, you can leave them out or use reported speech. If you do know how to use speech marks, perhaps you can spice up your story by including some direct speech.

6: Write a fable

Do you know what a **fable** is? It's a story with a moral at the end, which means it has a message about what you should do in life.

Fables are usually written about animals, to make the message simple. Here's an example:

There was once a lioness and her cubs. The first cub was boisterous, and often fell into streams and ditches. The second cub was always careful and obedient, and rather boring. The third cub was so shy that he never let go of his mother's tail.

One day they went off hunting in the bush, hoping to catch a small deer.

"There's one," said the lioness. "See if you can catch it!"

The first cub gave a great whoop and leaped so high that he fell into the river, and frightened the small deer away.

The third cub started wailing, and hid behind a large cactus.

The second cub waited patiently and then tracked down the deer so that they could all eat supper.

Moral: Look before you leap. (But life would be boring if we were all the same!)

Get ready

1. How does the first sentence suggest that this is not a factual account?

    _____

2. Why are there three cubs?

    _____

3. Who is the only character to use direct speech?

    _____

4. Which phrases give humour to the story?

    _____

5. What other wording could you use for the moral of the fable?

    _____

Now you write a fable, using animals as the characters.

You'll probably need to think up your moral first, so you can write your story round it.

_____

_____

_____

_____

_____

_____

_____

_____

Moral:_____

Have a go

Find some fables written by Aesop, who was an ancient Greek, or by La Fontaine, who was a French writer. Then write a modern version of one of them, using people rather than animals.

Teacher's tips

Humour could be created by situations or perhaps by word choice. Re-read the fable and think about these examples of humour to help answer question 4.

7: Rewrite a legend

Can you define what a **legend** is? It's a story handed down from the past, which may not be true in its details, but has important truths to tell us.

Read this brief version of the legend of Sir Gawain and the Green Knight.

One Christmas, King Arthur and his knights of the Round Table were sitting round a feast in Camelot. Suddenly, in rode a green knight on a green horse, and challenged King Arthur's men to test their bravery and their honour. The youngest knight was Sir Gawain, and he rose to accept the challenge. The green knight told Gawain to chop off his head, but to return in a year to have the same done to him. Gawain did the deed, to prove his bravery, and the green knight rode off with his head tucked underneath his arm.

A year later, Gawain rode off to find the green knight and keep his promise. He found a magical castle in a wood, and was invited to stay the night. Three times the lady of the castle visited Gawain to tempt him, but three times he kept his honour. In the end he accepted her green belt, to keep him safe.

Gawain then rode on and found the green knight, who three times raised his sword to chop off Gawain's head. But he spared Gawain, in recognition of the three times that Gawain had resisted his wife. The green knight let him keep the green belt, in memory of the trial of his chivalry, and Gawain returned to Arthur, to narrate his adventure.

Get ready

1. Do you think King Arthur and Sir Gawain really existed?

_____

2. Do you think that the green knight really existed?

_____

3. Which qualities of knightly behaviour was the green knight testing?

_____

4. Why was Gawain spared three times?

_____

Let's practise

Try rewriting this legend as a modern story. You should keep the elements of being tested for bravery, and keeping your honour. But make the setting and the characters modern. You will need to continue on a separate piece of paper.

Have a go

Find more legends about King Arthur and his knights of the Round Table.

Find more versions of the Sir Gawain story, for instance in the long poem by Tennyson.

Research the history of Camelot on the Internet.

Teacher's tips

A big clue to help you answer question 1 and question 2 is in the introduction, where you are told what a legend is. Read this again if you get stuck on either question.

8: Retelling Shakespeare

Shakespeare's plays are really difficult to read, aren't they? Luckily, however, there are lots of retellings of the plays that make the stories easier to understand.

Here's just a bit from *Romeo and Juliet*, which we've managed to explain in modern English.

Juliet How camest thou hither, tell me, and wherefore? The orchard walls are high and hard to climb, And the place death, considering who thou art, If any of my kinsmen find thee here.	*How did you get here?* *The orchard walls are high and hard to climb,* *And dangerous, considering who you are,* *If any of my family find you here.*
Romeo With love's light wings did I o'erperch these walls; For stony limits cannot hold love out, And what love can do, that dares love attempt: Therefore thy kinsmen are no stop to me.	*Love helped me climb the walls;* *These stones can't keep love out,* *Love will dare to do anything,* *So your family are not about to stop me.*

 Get ready

1   Which version was easier to understand?

_____

2   Which version had more poetic langage?

_____

3   Does it help to read the Shakespeare version aloud?

_____

Let's practise

The following speech is from the same play. Try to explain in modern English what the Nurse is saying.

Nurse

Now afore God, I am so vexed that every part about me quivers. Scurvy knave! Pray you, sir, a word. And as I told you, my young lady bid me enquire you out. What she bid me say I will keep to myself: but first let me tell ye, if ye should lead her in a fool's paradise, as they say, it were a very gross kind of behaviour, as they say: for the gentlewoman is young; and therefore, if you should deal double with her, truly it were an ill thing to be offered to any gentlewoman, and very weak dealing.

_____

_____

_____

_____

_____

_____

_____

_____

_____

Have a go

Find some retellings of Shakespeare's plays; there are some great versions in cartoon strips! Try comparing them with the original text, so that you can work out what the original words mean.

Teacher's tips

If you get stuck figuring out what the Nurse is saying, maybe you could get some help from the internet?

9: Compare a book and a film

Have any of your favourite books been made into films? Which version did you prefer? Why?

Here's a chart to help you work out what you prefer about each version. We've filled in this one for *Jane Eyre*.

<u>Prefer about the book</u> Jane is short and plain Rochester is a brooding character	<u>Dislike in the film</u> Jane is too tall and too pretty Rochester is too good-looking
<u>Dislike about the book</u> Long to read	<u>Prefer in the film</u> Shorter in film Film settings in Derbyshire Dramatic contrasts of light and shade

Get ready

1 Do you create pictures of the characters in your head, when you read?

2 Does the setting of a film help you imagine the landscape?

3 Do you notice the music they use for film scores?

Let's practise

Compare the film version with a book that you've read, for example a Harry Potter book or *Lord of the Rings*, or a Roald Dahl story. Use the same chart to help you.

Prefer about the book	Dislike in the film
Dislike about the book	**Prefer in the film**

Have a go

Find a review of a film of a book, where you know both versions. Do you agree with the review, or do you have a different opinion?

Teacher's tips

Questions that might help: What was a character like in the book and did the actor/actress show him/her the way you expected? Were bits of the book left out or did the film bring to life any events?

10: Write a book review

Do you ever read book reviews in magazines or on the Internet, to find out about books you might enjoy?

Here's a review of a children's book that was shortlisted for the *Guardian* Children's Book Award.

The Fire-Eaters
by David Almond
Hodder Children's Books

Set in 1950s Tyneside, in the build-up to the Cuban missile crisis, David Almond's novel shows what a subtle writer he is and how carefully and poetically he uses language.

As Bobby Burns turns 11, his life becomes more complicated. Not only does he have to face the new world of grammar school, with its arcane codes of behaviour and its bullying, but he is anxious about his sick father and has a growing awareness of social differences and the need to maintain friendships across them.

Almond makes familiar issues fresh; his characters are finely drawn and his depiction of place perfectly realised.

Get ready

1 What does the beginning of the first paragraph tell the reader?

_____

2 What is the purpose of the second paragraph?

_____

3 What comments are made about the author's style?

_____

_____

4 Did the reviewer like the book?

_____

Let's practise

Now write your own review. Use this plan to
organise your paragraphs, if it helps:

The setting of this book is _____

_____

_____

The plot is about _____

_____

_____

The author's style is _____

_____

My conclusion is _____

_____

_____

Have a go

Read reviews of children's books in magazines and in newspapers.
Do they express views both for and against? Do they make you want
to read the book?

Teacher's tips

The review may have a couple of words you're not sure about. The word *arcane*
means mysterious and the word *depiction* means the way something is shown or
described. If you're not sure about *subtle* . . . it's the opposite of obvious.

A blurb on a book cover is different from a review, because it serves a different purpose. Its aim is to persuade you to buy and read the book.

Here's the blurb from the same book as in Unit 10, *The Fire-Eaters* by David Almond.

There he was, below the bridge, half-naked, eyes blazing. He had a pair of burning torches. He ran them back and forth across his skin. He sipped from a bottle, breathed across a torch, and fire and fumes leapt from his lips. The air was filled with the scent of paraffin. He breathed again, a great high spreading flag of fire. He glared. He roared like an animal.

That summer, life had seemed perfect for Bobby Burns. But now it's autumn and the winds of change are blowing hard. Bobby's dad is mysteriously ill. His new school is a cold and cruel place. And worse: nuclear war may be about to start. But Bobby has a wonder-working friend called Ailsa Spink. And he's found the fire-eater, a devil called McNulty. What can they do together on Bobby's beach? Is it possible to work miracles? Will they be able to transform the world?

Get ready

1 Why is the first paragraph in italics?

_____

2 What is the effect of the questions in the second paragraph?

_____

3 Which did you find more persuasive: the book review or the cover blurb?

_____

Write a new cover blurb for a book you've enjoyed. Remember the blurb has to sell the book, so it should be really positive – and short enough to fit on the back of the book! You could add some illustrations round the edge, to give an idea of the plot and the characters.

Have a go

Look at the cover blurbs of books you've enjoyed. Could you improve on any of them? If so, you could send your blurb to the publisher of the book!

Teacher's tips

To help you with question 1, think about where the writing may have come from. When you write your own blurb, be careful not to tell the reader how the book ends! Just give them enough to want to read it!

12: Write an advert

Have you ever listened to an advert on the radio? It's different from an advert on TV or in a magazine as there aren't any pictures. All the **persuasion** has to be in the words.

Read the example below: it's a radio advert for a new kind of umbrella. Can you see how each paragraph adds to the persuasion?

Do you hate rainy days? Do you hate going out with your old umbrella in the cold and the wet?

Well, here's a way of cheering up those splishy-splashy cold wet days. It will put a smile on your face, and a glow in your heart.

Our umbrellas are completely different. They have a heating filament in them, to keep your hands warm and your face aglow. Imagine those patio heaters beaming warmth down on your head. Well, these are just the same, but you carry them with you!

Where can you get hold of one of these amazing inventions? Go to our website, www.hotumbrellas.co.uk, and find out how to cheer up your winter days. You'll never walk alone again!

1 What is the purpose of the first paragraph?

_____

2 What does the second paragraph do?

_____

3 What does the third paragraph do?

_____

4 What is the purpose of the fourth paragraph?

_____

Let's practise

Now we want you to invent a new everyday object, and write a radio advert for it. Follow the plan of four paragraphs, each serving a similar purpose to the model opposite.

Have a go

Did you enjoy the idea of inventing something new? The key thing is to identify a need, then try to answer the need. So think of a new service to offer on your mobile phone, and write an advert to persuade your friends of the benefits it could bring.

Teacher's tips

When you write your own advert, remember to include some questions to help persuade your listeners. Include lots of positive words and remember to talk to the listeners using words like 'you' and 'your'.

13: Write an explanation

Here's a real invention that will save energy rather than wasting heat!

On the label there's an **explanation** of how the product works, written to help the people who've just bought it.

This explanation tells you how to use our special kettle, which is designed to be eco-friendly.

The special feature of this kettle is that it has two chambers, one to store water and one to heat water. You release water from one chamber into the other by pressing the special valve on the top of the kettle. Then you only heat the water you need!

So all you have to do to make this kettle work is fill the main chamber with enough water to see you through the morning. Then each time you want to heat water for a cup of coffee, press the valve to release enough water to heat that one cup.

The benefits are that it saves you water; it saves you time; it saves you energy.

1 What tense is used for the verbs in the explanation?

_____

2 What would have helped you to understand how it works?

_____

3 Were you persuaded that it was a good idea? If so, what was it that persuaded you?

_____

 **Let's practise**

Now write your own explanation of how a particular gadget works in your home. Imagine your audience has never used this gadget before, but you have to use words not pictures to explain how it works.

This explanation tells you how _____

_____

The special feature _____

_____

_____

So all you have to do _____

_____

The benefits are _____

_____

 **Have a go**

Try inventing a new gadget for saving energy around the home. Write an explanation for the householder of how to use the gadget, and what the benefits are for the environment.

Teacher's tips

Remember, a verb is a doing word like *has* or *tell*. For question 2, think about something other than words.

What's special about how instructions are written? Instructions **tell you what to do**, so rather than using the present tense as in an explanation, they use the command form of the verb: do this, check that, etc. We call this form of the verb the **imperative**.

Instructions for flying

a space capsule

What you need:
Space suit
Ignition key
Map of outer space
Supplies to last the journey

What to do:
1 Make sure your space suit has been thoroughly sterilised.
2 Store your supplies in the fridge.
3 Check that you put the cat out before you lock the door.
4 Put the map on the ledge in front of you.
5 Fasten your seat belt.
6 Put the engine into gear.
7 Press the accelerator.
8 Count down and lift off!

Get ready

1 What are the two parts of the instructions?

_____

2 What parts of speech are used for the two sections?

_____

3 What punctuation is used for the two sections?

_____

 **Let's practise**

Your job is to write instructions for a team walking to the South Pole.

What will they need? What will they need to do to prepare for the journey?

What you need: _____

_____

_____

_____

What to do: _____

_____

_____

_____

_____

_____

 **Have a go**

Write instructions for your next family holiday. What does everyone need to take? What do they need to do to prepare for the journey?

Teacher's tips

To answer the questions in Get ready, look at the two columns in the rocket. Remember, parts of speech are things like verbs, nouns and adjectives.

Do you know what a **thesaurus** is? It's like a dictionary, but rather than giving the meaning for each word, it gives you lots of other words that mean the same thing. This can really help with your writing.

Look at the entries below for three words beginning with **sh**:

---

shiny *adjective*
bright, gleaming, glossy, polished
opposite dull

shiver *verb*
to quiver, to shake, to shudder, to tremble

shock *verb*
1 to alarm, to frighten, to startle, to stun, to surprise
2 to disgust, to offend, to upset

Get ready

1 What comes after each word in italics? _____

2 Which kind of word is given an opposite meaning? _____

3 Which word has two slightly different meanings? _____

4 Choose one of the verbs, and use it in a sentence to show its meaning.

_____

Now we want you to fill in lists of
words that mean the same as
these key words.

---

small *adjective*

_____

opposite _____

walk *verb*

_____

shout *verb*

_____

 **Have a go**

Have you got a thesaurus at home? If not, see if you can take one home
from school.

Then play a game with your family or friends, reading out words from the
thesaurus, and seeing how many words everyone can list that mean the same.

Teacher's tips

To show the meaning of *hid*, the sentence *I hid in the cave* is unclear. Here, the word
hid could mean *walked, ran* or *slipped*. A better sentence would be *I hid in the cave
so they wouldn't find me.*

We all know about using commas in lists. But it's also very common to use commas to separate off an 'aside', instead of using brackets.

Look at these examples. See how they must have punctuation at both the beginning and the end of the 'aside'.

Queen Elizabeth I, who came to the throne in 1558, reigned for 45 years.

My father, who had a terrible cold, sneezed all day long.

The bird, sitting on the wire above our house, had a beautiful song.

These two colours, red and blue, are always the most popular.

The biggest actor (the one with the beard) had the loudest voice.

The fat old cook — you should have seen him! — could hardly fit into the kitchen.

Get ready

Can you see that there's a slight difference between the examples?

- The ones with **commas** add extra information or an explanation, which is fairly essential to the sentence.

- Where you use **brackets**, the aside is less important, and could be missed out altogether.

- With **dashes**, the sense is quite informal, so you should avoid dashes in more formal writing.

Let's practise

Write some examples of these three kinds of punctuation. Make sure you include the closing punctuation mark as well as the opening one.

Commas _____

_____

_____

Brackets _____

_____

_____

Dashes _____

_____

_____

Have a go

Look in your reading for examples of commas, brackets and dashes used for 'asides'.

Teacher's tips

Try removing the section of the sentence between the commas, brackets or dashes in these examples. You'll see that the sentences still make complete sense. For example, *Queen Elizabeth reigned for 45 years*. The sections just add extra information.

Do you know the difference between autobiography and biography? **Autobiography** is when someone writes their own life story. **Biography** is when someone writes the story of someone else's life.

Here is an example of a short autobiography by a famous singer.

I was born in a small terraced house in the backstreets of Salford, near Manchester. My father was away travelling all the time, and my mother had to go out to work. So I was mainly brought up by my grandmother, who lived with us.

When I was at school, I was always misbehaving. I wasn't good at lessons, and all I wanted to do was play music. I used to go off with my mates, and we'd practise in the basement of my friend Rod, who had a much bigger house than the rest of us.

What changed it all was when we left school. We sent a tape of one of our recordings to this record company. At first we heard nothing, so we started to give up on our chances. But then we were playing at a gig in Deansgate, and a guy came up to us after, saying he'd heard our tape and had come to hear what we were really like.

And I've never looked back since. We got a recording contract, and started travelling to all the big clubs round the country. Then I went solo, and you see my name around everywhere.

Get ready

1 How can you tell the singer is writing about his or her own life?

_____

2 What tense are the verbs: past, present or future?

_____

3 What period is the first paragraph about?

_____

4 When was the turning point for this singer?

_____

Let's practise

Try to turn this autobiography into a biography.

This means turning all the 'first person' writing into 'third person'. You'll also have to decide if the singer is male or female, and choose a name. You may need to continue on a separate piece of paper.

_____ was born in a small terraced house in the

backstreets of Salford, near Manchester. _____

_____

_____

_____

_____

_____

_____

_____

Have a go

Write a brief version of your own autobiography. Plan out which event you'll cover in each photograph. Who will be your audience? How can you make them interested in your life?

Teacher's tips

You don't have to use exactly the same sentence structures or order as the autobiography does in your biography. For example, the sentences _My father was travelling ... with us_ could start _He was raised by his grandmother because ..._

18: Write a newspaper article

What's special about newspaper writing?

It usually has to grab people's attention, and make them think about issues, because it's there to sell newspapers.

Polar bears melt in the heat!

Should polar bears be kept in zoos in this scorching climate? How can we justify keeping them here?

Our reporter went down to the local zoo to see how the polar bears are coping in this heat. We have to admit that they are very well looked after. The keepers give them lots of care and attention, and give them their natural diet of fresh fish. And it does give us all the opportunity to see polar bears close up.

But the bears don't look happy in the heat. Their natural habitat is many degrees colder, and they are used to far more empty space. If we want children to see how these animals behave, there are plenty of nature films on television that we can all watch.

The zoo is organising an open day on 15 September, from 10a.m. to 3p.m., for schools to visit and ask the keepers about how they look after the animals. You are all welcome to come and give your views then!

Use a different colour to highlight or underline each of the following features.

1   Headline to grab your attention

2   Leading questions to draw you in

3   Positive points of view in the first main paragraph

4   Opposing points of view in the next paragraph

5   Concluding paragraph of information

Think of another controversial issue and write an article about it for your local newspaper.

Make sure you include a headline, leading questions, and separate paragraphs for the different points of view.

Have a go

Do you have a school newsletter or website that would welcome articles? Write a piece, with different points of view, to submit.

Teacher's tips

To help you keep track of all the different features, why don't you highlight or underline each different feature in a different colour? Remember to indicate next to questions 1–5 what colour each feature is.

Have you ever written a letter about an issue you feel strongly about?

Here's what I wrote to the zoo after I read the newspaper article in Unit 18.

1 The Square,
Dunbarton DB1 3QX

21 August 2007

Dear Sir/Madam,

I want to write to you about the polar bears you keep in your zoo.

It has been so hot this summer that they must have been really suffering. I think that polar bears should live in their natural habitat, because they are suited to living on the ice and catching their fish from the sea.

I suppose there's an argument for letting the local children see what polar bears are really like. But if we want to see polar bears these days, we can see them on nature films.

Please tell me why you don't send your bears back to the habitat where they belong.

Yours truly,
Megan Griffiths

Get ready

Fill in this grid with the reasons Megan gives for and against keeping polar bears in the zoo. Which list of reasons is longer?

Against zoos	For zoos

Can you think of something in your neighbourhood that you feel strongly about?

Make a list of the points you want to make, as in the grid opposite.

Then write a letter, giving your reasoned point of view. And don't be too rude, or you won't get a reply!

Have a go

Have you any strong views about wildlife? Try writing a letter to the World Wildlife Fund (WWF), clearly stating your points of view.

Teacher's tips

Remember to put your address in the top right hand corner and the date on the left. Also think carefully about how to address the person you are writing to and how to end your letter.

20: Formal and informal English

There are reasons why people use formal English for important texts. It's because the text has to look important, and the meaning has to be very clear.

Here is a set of rules that go out with the Key Stage 2 tests.

Mark schemes for English tests

1   The teacher's notes explain how pupils' answers will be marked.

2   The first guide is the 'assessment focus' sections, which describe what makes a good answer.

3   The notes then say how many marks can be awarded for different levels of answer.

4   They also give examples of pupils' handwritten answers, and explain how many marks should be given to each.

5   The marks are then converted to a scale of level 3 to level 5.

6   The tests are marked by external markers, following the mark schemes in these notes.

7   The results are sent to schools afterwards.

Get ready

1   How are the rules laid out? _____

2   List any **passive** verb forms you can find. (For example, 'answers will be marked'.) _____

_____

_____

3   Who do you think is the audience for this text?

_____

Let's practise

Now let's convert this into an informal explanation of how the tests are marked.

Imagine you're explaining to a friend how your tests will be marked. You'll want to change passive verbs into active verbs. We've given you a start . . .

I read in the teacher's notes how the markers are going to mark our tests.

They read the 'assessment focus' sections, to find out _____

_____

_____

_____

_____

_____

_____

_____

Have a go

Write a list of notes to help the pupils in your school prepare for sitting the tests. What do they need to do before the tests, and what do they need to take with them?

Make the list quite formal, so that it can be put on the school noticeboard.

Teacher's tips

The mark scheme on page 90 provides a list of steps for markers to follow when they mark the tests. The information you tell your friend is based on these steps. You may find words like *then* and *next* useful.

How have I done?

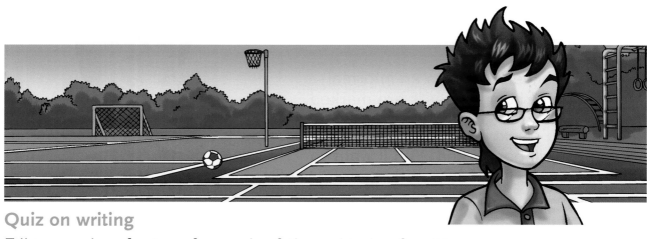

Quiz on writing

Fill in one key feature for each of these kinds of writing:

1. Limerick _____

2. Playscript _____

3. Direct speech _____

4. Reported speech _____

5. Story plan _____

6. Fable _____

7. Legend _____

8. Shakespeare _____

9. Book review _____

10. Cover blurb _____

11. Advert _____

12. Thesaurus _____

13. Autobiography _____

14. Explanation _____

15. Instructions _____

16. Newspaper article _____

17. Point of view _____

18. Formal English _____

Quiz on punctuation

Punctuate these sentences:

1 The king who was very old could not kneel down in his tight breeches

_____

2 He asked the queen could you help me please

_____

3 Not on your life she said

_____

4 I have it in mind to steal the throne if youre not up to it

_____

5 So without a pause she vaulted over the poor man and plonked herself on the throne

_____

6 The courtiers cried out whats all this

_____

7 They held a quick referendum or quiz would people prefer a king or a queen

_____

8 The result of the vote was six for the king and four for the queen

_____

9 So in the end the king got himself back on the throne in the nick of time

_____

10 Never mind he said to the queen. Better luck next time

_____

Teacher's tips

If you need to remind yourself of anything, the Contents page at the start of the book might help you turn to the correct page for help. When punctuating, take your time and check over what you write!

Maths

- Step-by-step exercises
- Master the core skills

1: Numbers to 1 000 000

We have a very clever way of writing numbers. Using just the digits 0, 1, 2, 3, 4, 5, 6, 7, 8 and 9 we can write any numbers we like. The important thing to remember is **where** each digit is placed in the number.

M	HTh	TTh	Th	H	T	U
	3	9	0	4	5	7

We sometimes use a space or a comma to separate the thousands digits from the hundreds, tens and units digits, like this **390 457** or **390,457.** This can help us to say or write the number more easily.

Three hundred and ninety **thousand** four hundred and fifty seven

⬤ Get ready

Write these numbers in words.

1 53 132 _____

2 17 333 _____

3 370 311 _____

4 100 006 _____

5 505 050 _____

6 609 009 _____

7 763 207 _____

Let's practise

Write the value of the underlined digit. One has been done for you.

8 6̲68 375   six hundred thousand

9 468 3̲82   _____

10 8̲30 621   _____

11 496̲ 582   _____

12 2̲90 303   _____

13 595 6̲29   _____

14 Continue each sequence by counting on in equal steps.

374 848	472 592	308 962
375 848	482 592	308 972
376 848	492 592	308 982
377 848	_____	_____
_____	_____	_____
_____	_____	_____
_____	_____	_____

 **Have a go**

Write down the last six digits of your telephone number. Say this as a number in words. How many more would you need to add to your number to reach one million?

Teacher's tips

A sequence is when a series of numbers are changed by the same action each time, such as adding 100 or subtracting 10. To find sequences with very large numbers it can be useful to write them in columns.

2: Rounding

To round numbers you must decide what you are rounding **to**.

The number
could be rounded to...
or to
or to
or to

66259
66260 (to the nearest 10)
66300 (to the nearest 100)
66000 (to the nearest 1000)
70000 (to the nearest 10000)

Look at the digit to the right of the one you are rounding to. If it is 5 or larger, round up. If it is less than 5, round down.

So when rounding **66259** to the nearest 10, look at the digit to the right of the tens column. Here it is a **9** so you round up to 66260, rather than down to 66250.

Get ready

Round these numbers to the nearest 10.

1 34386 _____

2 83354 _____

3 25315 _____

4 275172 _____

5 194204 _____

6 174205 _____

Round these numbers to the nearest 100.

7 37336 _____

8 710283 _____

9 376850 _____

10 363472 _____

Let's practise

11 Complete this table to round to the nearest 10, 100, 1000, 10 000 and 100 000.

Rounded to the nearest:	274 482	193 255	375 985
10	274 480		
100	274 500		
1000	274 000		
10 000			
100 000			

Answer these questions.

12 What is the smallest number that, when rounded to the nearest 100, is 600? _____

13 What is the largest number that, when rounded to the nearest 100, is 1100? _____

14 What is the smallest number that, when rounded to the nearest 1000, is 5000? _____

15 What is the largest number that, when rounded to the nearest 10 000, is 90 000? _____

Have a go

Numbers in newspapers are often rounded, such as 'Man wins £100 000' or '57 000 people at the match'. Look for examples in your own magazine, newspaper or online.

Teacher's tips

Rounding makes numbers easier to work with, and helps give an order of magnitude. Think about what the information is being used for, and who is using it, when deciding how much to round a number to.

3: Multiples and common multiples

Here are some **multiples of 6**.

6, 12, 18, 24, 30, 36, 42, 48, 54, 60, 66, 72...

Here are some **multiples of 8**.

8, 16, 24, 32, 40, 48, 56, 64, 72, 80, 88, 96...

Some numbers are multiples of both 6 and 8. We call them **common multiples** of 6 and 8. Examples are 24, 48, 72 and so on.

Get ready

1   List the first twelve multiples of 3.

　　　3 __ __ __ __ __ __ __ __ __ __ __

2   List the first twelve multiples of 6.

　　　6 __ __ __ __ __ __ __ __ __ __ __

3   List the first twelve multiples of 4.

　　　4 __ __ __ __ __ __ __ __ __ __ __

4   Now write the first six common multiples of **3 and 6**.

　　　__ __ __ __ __ __

5   Write the first three common multiples of **3 and 4**.

　　　__ __ __

Let's practise

The first common multiple is known as the **lowest common multiple**.

Find the lowest common multiple of these pairs.

6 4 and 6 _____

7 2 and 3 _____

8 5 and 2 _____

9 3 and 10 _____

10 3 and 5 _____

11 10 and 4 _____

12 3 and 7 _____

13 7 and 8 _____

You can find common multiples of more than two numbers, e.g. the multiple of 12 is common to the 2, 3, 4, 6 and 12 times tables so we say 12 is a common multiple of 2, 3, 4, 6 and 12.

Find the lowest common multiple of these.

14 2, 4 and 7 _____

15 2, 3, 5, 6 and 10 _____

16 2, 4, 5 and 10 _____

17 2, 3, 4, 6, 8 and 12 _____

 **Have a go**

Roll two dice and say a common multiple of the two numbers rolled. Do this many times and write down the lowest common multiple each time. What is the highest number you will write down? Which numbers between 1 and 10 won't you write down?

Teacher's tips

The better you know your times tables the easier you will find it to spot multiples of numbers, and recognise patterns. For instance, that any 2-digit number where the sum of the digits is 9, is a multiple of 9.

4: Factors and primes

A **factor** is a number that divides into another without a remainder. For example, 5 is a factor of 15 as it divides into it exactly.

A **prime number** is a number that only has two factors, itself and 1.

15 is not a prime number as it has four factors, 1, 3, 5 and 15.

17 is prime as it only has the factors 1 and 17.

Get ready

Say whether each statement is **true** or **false**.

1. 5 is a factor of 20. _____

2. 3 is a factor of 10. _____

3. 7 is a factor of 14 and 21. _____

4. 25 has the factors 1, 5 and 25. _____

5. 19 has the factors 1, 3 and 19. _____

6. 7 is a prime number as it only has the factors 1 and 7.

    _____

7. 9 is prime as it only has the factor 1 and 9. _____

8. 21 is non-prime as it has the factors 1, 3, 7 and 21.

    _____

9. 2, 3, 5 and 7 are prime numbers as they only have two factors each. _____

 Let's practise

Begin by colouring the number 1 in the 100 square below.

Next colour the multiples of 2 starting with 4.

Then colour the multiples of 3 starting with 6.

Then colour the multiples of 4 starting with 8 and so on.

Keep going for multiples of 5, 6, 7, 8, 9, 10, 11 and 12, always starting with the second multiple.

1	2	3	4	5	6	7	8	9	10
11	12	13	14	15	16	17	18	19	20
21	22	23	24	25	26	27	28	29	30
31	32	33	34	35	36	37	38	39	40
41	42	43	44	45	46	47	48	49	50
51	52	53	54	55	56	57	58	59	60
61	62	63	64	65	66	67	68	69	70
71	72	73	74	75	76	77	78	79	80
81	82	83	84	85	86	87	88	89	90
91	92	93	94	95	96	97	98	99	100

10 Write a list of the uncoloured numbers. _____

_____

11 What is special about them? _____

 **Have a go**

Look on the internet to find a list of all the prime numbers up to 100. Compare them with your list of numbers.

Teacher's tips

It's very useful to know prime numbers to 100 because if you come across them in a problem, such as trying to simplify a fraction, you will know that they have no factors other than themselves and 1.

5: Written addition

When using a written method for adding numbers, make sure you line the digits up correctly, so that the tens of thousands, thousands, hundreds, tens and ones digits are lined up, like this.

49365 + 53267

```
  4 9 3 6 5
+ 5 3 2 6 7
```

It can help to work from right to left, adding the digits in each column and carrying, like this.

```
  4 9 3 6 5
+ 5 3 2 6 7
  ₁  ₁ ₁
1 0 2 6 3 2
```

 Get ready

Find these totals using a written method. Make an approximation first and use it to check your answer each time.

①
```
  3 3 6 2 4
+   5 3 5 3
_____
_____
```

②
```
  2 6 1 3 5
+   7 2 2 7
_____
_____
```

③
```
  6 5 3 5 3
+ 1 5 7 2 8
_____
_____
```

④
```
  7 3 2 2 5
+ 1 3 5 6 3
_____
_____
```

⑤
```
  8 9 3 7 3
+ 1 6 7 6 5
_____
_____
```

⑥
```
  2 6 0 1 7
  3 3 2 9 5
+ 5 2 9 1 5
_____
_____
```

 **Let's practise**

Write out these questions in columns and answer them using a written method. Remember to line up the digits correctly.

7 54 769 + 4321

10 35 382 + 26 509

8 41 758 + 46 498

11 6437 + 84 684

9 52 475 + 16 385

12 36 709 + 94 591

 **Have a go**

Look in a newspaper or magazine for the attendances at football matches in the Premier League. Add them all up to see how many people went to the matches altogether.

Teacher's tips

Always write a small '1', as shown on page 104, whenever you have to carry an extra '1 lot of ten/hundred/thousand', to remind you to add that '1 lot of _' to the numbers already in the column.

6: Written subtraction

When using a written method for subtracting numbers, make sure you line the digits up correctly, so that digits are lined up, like this.

37 164 – 17 237

```
  3 7 1 6 4
– 1 7 2 3 7
```

It can help to work from right to left, borrowing from the column to the left if there aren't enough in that column, like this.

```
  2  16  1  5  1
  3  7  1  6  4
– 1  7  2  3  7
  1  9  9  2  7
```

Get ready

Answer these subtractions using a written method. Make an approximation first and use it to check your answer each time.

1
```
  9 6 6 8 6
– 6 9 4 5 3
_____
```

4
```
  7 1 1 4 3
– 5 2 3 8 6
_____
```

2
```
  8 1 5 3 5
– 6 1 2 3 8
_____
```

5
```
  5 3 6 2 3
– 3 7 8 5 4
_____
```

3
```
  4 6 7 4 7
– 2 9 2 9 8
_____
```

6
```
  6 0 4 2 1
– 2 5 2 3 9
_____
```

Write out these questions in columns and answer them using a written method.

7 62 754 – 39 676

10 57 583 – 32 667

8 87 441 – 43 793

11 75 830 – 48 991

9 70 634 – 51 759

12 70 804 – 34 539

Have a go

Make as many different 5-digit numbers as you can, using the digits 4, 4, 5, 1 and 9. Choose pairs of the numbers and find the difference by subtracting. What is the largest difference you can find?

Teacher's tips

When borrowing '1 lot of _' from the column to the left, remember not only to write the '1' next to the number it's been 'lent' to, but also to decrease the number that you've borrowed it from by 1.

7: Times tables

How well do you know your times tables? Try to learn all your times tables up to 12 × 12.

A multiplication tables grid can help you keep a check of which facts you're sure of. Multiply the number in the left hand column by the number at the top of each column. See how many you know.

Get ready

1 Fill in the answers to check how well you know your times tables. Try them out of order, by choosing any box to fill in.

×	1	2	3	4	5	6	7	8	9	10	11	12
1												
2	2											
3										30		
4												
5												
6				24								
7												
8												
9												
10												
11												
12												

Check and mark your answers. Colour all the correct answers yellow and the wrong answers red.

Let's practise

Answer these questions as quickly as you can.

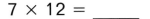

7 × 12 = _____	7 × 7 = _____	8 × 9 = _____
12 × 7 = _____	11 × 4 = _____	8 × 8 = _____
6 × 6 = _____	12 × 12 = _____	9 × 9 = _____
12 × 5 = _____	8 × 11 = _____	11 × 12 = _____
8 × 7 = _____	11 × 0 = _____	6 × 1 = _____
11 × 9 = _____	12 × 10 = _____	7 × 0 = _____
12 × 9 = _____	5 × 7 = _____	6 × 7 = _____
9 × 10 = _____	8 × 3 = _____	5 × 6 = _____
4 × 8 = _____	12 × 9 = _____	8 × 6 = _____
11 × 3 = _____	5 × 12 = _____	12 × 8 = _____
9 × 7 = _____	11 × 6 = _____	11 × 11 = _____

You also need to make sure that you can answer related division questions for each fact. For example, if you know that 6 × 8 = 48 and 8 × 6 = 48 then you should know that 48 ÷ 8 = 6 and 48 ÷ 6 = 8.

Have a go

Make a list of all the answers you coloured red and write the correct answers. These are facts that you must work harder to learn. Make cards with the answers on one side and the questions on the other to help you practise recalling the facts.

Teacher's tips

Learn the most common tables – 2, 3, 5 and 10 to start. Then learn all the squares of numbers to 12. Once you've done this you will have enough tables learned to quickly calculate most others in your head.

When multiplying by 10, 100 or 1000 move each digit one, two or three places to the left as shown.

Hth	Tth	Th	H	T	U
			5	2	9

529 × 10 =

Hth	Tth	Th	H	T	U
		5	2	9	0

529 × 100 =

Hth	Tth	Th	H	T	U
	5	2	9	0	0

529 × 1000 =

Hth	Tth	Th	H	T	U
5	2	9	0	0	0

When dividing by 10, 100 or 1000 move each digit one, two or three places to the right as shown.

Hth	Tth	Th	H	T	U
5	2	9	0	0	0

529 000 ÷ 10 =

Hth	Tth	Th	H	T	U
	5	2	9	0	0

529 000 ÷ 100 =

Hth	Tth	Th	H	T	U
		5	2	9	0

529 000 ÷ 1000 =

Hth	Tth	Th	H	T	U
			5	2	9

Get ready

Answer these questions.

1. 373 × 10 = _____

2. 86 × 100 = _____

3. 68 × 1000 = _____

4. 673 × 100 = _____

5. 240 × 10 = _____

6. 9300 ÷ 10 = _____

7. 4200 ÷ 100 = _____

8. 844 000 ÷ 100 = _____

9. 19 000 ÷ 1000 = _____

10. 865 000 ÷ 100 = _____

Let's practise

Use what you know about multiplying by 10, 100 and 1000 to multiply by numbers like 20, 700, 4000, etc. First multiply by 2, 7 or 4 and then move the digits. Answer these questions. The first has been done for you.

11 $7 \times 300 = $ $7 \times 3 \times 100 = 21 \times 100 = 2100$

12 $8 \times 60 = $ _____

13 $4 \times 12\,000 = $ _____

14 $6000 \times 11 = $ _____

15 $900 \times 12 = $ _____

16 $60 \times 70 = $ _____

17 $700 \times 20 = $ _____

18 $5000 \times 5 = $ _____

19 $800 \times 70 = $ _____

20 $12 \times 7000 = $ _____

Have a go

'The answer is 24 000.'
Write as many different multiplication questions as you can that have this answer. Here are two examples.

$40 \times 600 = 24\,000$ $12 \times 2000 = 24\,000$

Teacher's tips

Mathematicians move the numbers not the decimal place (and they are correct!), but when multiplying or dividing by 10, 100 or 1000, moving the decimal point 1, 2 or 3 places to the left (division) or right (multiplication) is a quick 'cheat'.

9: Multiplication

To multiply large numbers we sometimes use a method called **long multiplication**.

Here is an example.

364 × 26

364 × 20
364 × 6

```
      3 6 4
    ×   2 6
    ———————
      7 2 8 0
  +   2 1 8 4
    ———————
      9 4 6 4
```

Another method used is called **grid multiplication**.

	300	60	4	
20	6000	1200	80	= 7280
6	1800	360	24	= 2184
				9464

 **Get ready**

Use the method you prefer to answer these multiplication questions.

1 153 × 12   **3** 857 × 16   **5** 4862 × 89

2 324 × 25   **4** 5478 × 27

Let's practise

Use a similar method to solve these problems.

6 A lorry is carrying 145 crates of cola. Each crate holds 24 bottles of cola. How many bottles altogether?

_____

7 A shop sells CDs costing £18. In one year they sell 3758 CDs. How much money do they get from selling them? _____

Have a go

Arrange these digits to make a multiplication question.

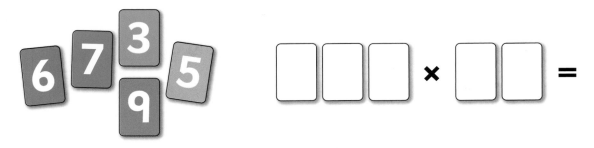

How many different questions and answers can you make?

Teacher's tips

Whichever method you choose to use it's really important to show your working, so you can go back and check your work. Estimate the answer before you start to see if yours looks right, or needs to be checked.

10: Division

There are different ways of dividing numbers. One of the methods used is called **short division**.

$$686 \div 4 = \quad 4\overline{)6^28\,6} \quad \overset{1\ 7\ 1\ r\ 2}{}$$

When a number doesn't divide exactly we can give the answer with a remainder, with fractions or as a decimal, like this.

$$686 \div 4 = 171\ r2 \quad \text{or} \quad 171\frac{2}{4} \quad \text{or} \quad 171\frac{1}{2}$$

$$\text{or} \quad 171.5$$

Get ready

Answer these division questions, giving your answers with remainders where necessary.

1. 891 ÷ 3 = _____

2. 356 ÷ 5 = _____

3. 127 ÷ 4 = _____

4. 463 ÷ 9 = _____

5. 337 ÷ 6 = _____

6. 195 ÷ 7 = _____

7. 295 ÷ 5 = _____

8. 784 ÷ 8 = _____

9. 667 ÷ 9 = _____

10. 376 ÷ 4 = _____

11. 462 ÷ 7 = _____

12. 808 ÷ 3 = _____

Let's practise

Answer these division questions giving a fraction in your answer.

13 155 ÷ 2 = _____

14 57 ÷ 4 = _____

15 213 ÷ 4 = _____

16 627 ÷ 2 = _____

17 243 ÷ 4 = _____

18 175 ÷ 4 = _____

Try dividing these 4-digit numbers.

19 1735 ÷ 5 = _____

20 1428 ÷ 4 = _____

21 2835 ÷ 3 = _____

22 1410 ÷ 6 = _____

23 1976 ÷ 8 = _____

24 5152 ÷ 7 = _____

25 1215 ÷ 9 = _____

Have a go

Use a calculator to divide each of these numbers by 9.

19   20   21   22   23   24   25   26   27   28   29

What do you notice about the answers?
Try to predict other answers, giving them as decimals.

Teacher's tips

Make sure you understand the difference between the numbers that may be 'carried over' when a number has extra 'lots of' that are added to the number to its right, and the final answer that may have a remainder.

11: Equivalent fractions

Fractions are said to be equivalent when they stand for the same amount, like $\frac{1}{2}$ and $\frac{2}{4}$.

You can multiply or divide the numerator (the top number) and the denominator (the bottom number) by the same number to get other equivalent fractions.

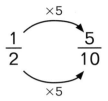 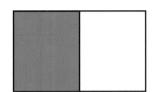 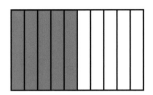

You can also use this method to help you compare fractions, such as $\frac{1}{2}$ and $\frac{4}{10}$. By converting $\frac{1}{2}$ to the equivalent fraction $\frac{5}{10}$ it makes it easier to see that $\frac{1}{2}$ is larger than $\frac{4}{10}$.

Get ready

For each pair, tick which fraction is larger. Change one of the fractions to an equivalent one if you need to.

1 $\frac{2}{5}$ $\frac{3}{10}$

2 $\frac{2}{3}$ $\frac{5}{6}$

3 $\frac{3}{4}$ $\frac{7}{8}$

4 $\frac{1}{3}$ $\frac{2}{9}$

5 $\frac{2}{3}$ $\frac{10}{12}$

6 $\frac{1}{2}$ $\frac{6}{14}$

Let's practise

7 Change each of these fractions to an equivalent one with the denominator 12.

$$\frac{1}{4} = \frac{\boxed{}}{12}$$

$$\frac{1}{3} = \frac{\boxed{}}{12}$$

$$\frac{1}{2} = \frac{\boxed{}}{12}$$

$$\frac{5}{6} = \frac{\boxed{}}{12}$$

$$\frac{3}{4} = \frac{\boxed{}}{12}$$

$$\frac{2}{3} = \frac{\boxed{}}{12}$$

Now use your answers to write the six original fractions in order, starting with the smallest.

_____ _____ _____ _____ _____ _____

8 Use the same method to help you order the fractions given below, smallest first. Change them so that they all have the denominator 20.

$$\frac{7}{10} \qquad \frac{4}{5} \qquad \frac{1}{2} \qquad \frac{3}{4} \qquad \frac{11}{20}$$

_____ _____ _____ _____ _____

Have a go

How could you compare the fractions $\frac{5}{8}$ and $\frac{7}{12}$ using a similar method?

Teacher's tips

A quick way to create a common denominator is to multiply both denominators by the largest denominator. Then multiply both numerators by the same number you've multiplied the denominators by. You'll end up with big numbers, but equivalent fractions.

A **mixed number**, like $1\frac{3}{4}$, contains a whole number and a fraction. They can be shown on a number line between whole numbers, like this.

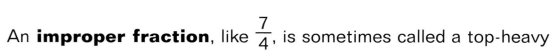

An **improper fraction**, like $\frac{7}{4}$, is sometimes called a top-heavy fraction because the numerator (top number) is larger than the denominator. Improper fractions, like mixed numbers are worth more than one whole.

Get ready

① Draw arrows to show the positions of these mixed numbers on this number line.

$$2\frac{3}{4} \qquad 4\frac{1}{4} \qquad 3\frac{1}{2} \qquad 1\frac{1}{4}$$

② $\frac{4}{4} \qquad \frac{8}{4} \qquad \frac{10}{4} \qquad \frac{13}{4} \qquad \frac{19}{4}$

Draw arrows to show the positions of the improper fractions above on the same line.

Write each mixed number as an improper fraction with the denominator (bottom number) 4. One has been done for you. Use the number line opposite to help you.

3 $1\frac{1}{4} = \frac{5}{4}$

6 $3\frac{1}{4} =$

4 $1\frac{3}{4} =$

7 $4\frac{1}{4} =$

5 $2\frac{2}{4} =$

8 $3\frac{3}{4} =$

Now write each improper fraction as a mixed number.

9 $\frac{9}{4} =$

12 $\frac{18}{4} =$

10 $\frac{6}{4} =$

13 $\frac{13}{4} =$

11 $\frac{11}{4} =$

14 $\frac{19}{4} =$

 Have a go

This number line is split into tenths. Find out how to write the marked positions as mixed numbers and improper fractions.

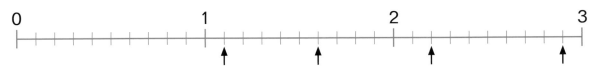

What do you notice?

Teacher's tips

A quick way to calculate mixed fractions is to multiply the number of units by the denominator, then add this number to the numerator, to give you the new numerator of the improper fraction. Think about why this works.

13: Decimals

Decimals are another way of writing fractions that have the denominator 10, 100, 1000 and so on. Look at these patterns.

Tenths:

$\frac{1}{10} = 0.1,$ $\frac{2}{10} = 0.2,$ $\frac{3}{10} = 0.3,$ $\frac{4}{10} = 0.4 \ldots$

$\frac{11}{10} = 1.1,$ $\frac{12}{10} = 1.2,$ $\frac{13}{10} = 1.3,$ $\frac{14}{10} = 1.4 \ldots$

Hundredths:

$\frac{1}{100} = 0.01,$ $\frac{2}{100} = 0.02,$ $\frac{3}{100} = 0.03,$ $\frac{4}{100} = 0.04 \ldots$

$\frac{11}{100} = 0.11,$ $\frac{12}{100} = 0.12,$ $\frac{13}{100} = 0.13,$ $\frac{14}{100} = 0.14 \ldots$

Write each of these fractions as a decimal.

1 $\frac{7}{10} = $ _____

5 $\frac{6}{100} = $ _____

2 $\frac{9}{100} = $ _____

6 $\frac{15}{100} = $ _____

3 $\frac{17}{100} = $ _____

7 $\frac{57}{100} = $ _____

4 $\frac{8}{10} = $ _____

8 $\frac{61}{100} = $ _____

Let's practise

Write each of these decimals as a fraction with the denominator 10 or 100.

9 0.8 =

13 0.48 =

10 0.07 =

14 6.4 =

11 1.2 =

15 0.05 =

12 0.27 =

16 0.99 =

Write each decimal as a fraction with the denominator 10 or 100 and then write the fraction in its simplest form.

17 0.5 =

20 0.25 =

18 0.05 =

21 0.75 =

19 0.6 =

22 0.04 =

 Have a go

Look on the internet. Find out how fractions with the denominator 1000, such as $\frac{7}{1000}$ and $\frac{325}{1000}$, are written as decimals.

Teacher's tips

With decimals the position of the digit is vital – just like whole numbers. Whole numbers **increase** – 10, 100, 1000 each column left of a decimal point, and decimals **decrease** – ten<u>ths</u>, hundred<u>ths</u>, thousand<u>ths</u> each column right of a decimal point.

14: Percentages

Just like fractions and decimals, percentages can be used to show parts of a whole. A **percentage** is a fraction with a **denominator** of 100, but written in a different way.

$$36\% \quad = \quad \frac{36}{100} \quad = \quad 0.36$$

Thirty-six **per cent** means thirty six **out of a hundred**.

We can place them all on a number line, like this.

0	10%	20%	30%	40%	50%	60%	70%	80%	90%	100%
0	0.1	0.2	0.3	0.4	0.5	0.6	0.7	0.8	0.9	1
0	$\frac{1}{10}$	$\frac{2}{10}$	$\frac{3}{10}$	$\frac{4}{10}$	$\frac{5}{10}$	$\frac{6}{10}$	$\frac{7}{10}$	$\frac{8}{10}$	$\frac{9}{10}$	1

Get ready

Write each of these fractions as a percentage.

1. $\dfrac{4}{100} =$ _____

2. $\dfrac{9}{100} =$ _____

3. $\dfrac{16}{100} =$ _____

4. $\dfrac{80}{100} =$ _____

5. $\dfrac{6}{100} =$ _____

6. $\dfrac{15}{100} =$ _____

7. $\dfrac{57}{100} =$ _____

8. $\dfrac{61}{100} =$ _____

Write each of these decimals as a fraction with the denominator 100 and then as a percentage. One has been done for you.

9 $0.8 = \dfrac{80}{100} = 80\%$

13 $0.48 = $ _____

10 $0.07 = $ _____

14 $0.4 = $ _____

11 $0.2 = $ _____

15 $0.05 = $ _____

12 $0.27 = $ _____

16 $0.99 = $ _____

Write each percentage as a fraction with the denominator 100 and then write the fraction in its simplest form.

17 $50\% = $ _____

20 $20\% = $ _____

18 $25\% = $ _____

21 $5\% = $ _____

19 $75\% = $ _____

22 $4\% = $ _____

 Have a go

Look through some newspapers and magazines for examples of when percentages are used. Cut out or make a list of the examples, e.g. Rooney is 100% fit, this yogurt is 4% fat, 50% sale, etc.

Write each percentage as a fraction with the denominator 100.

Teacher's tips

Don't get caught out when converting single-digit percentages or fractions of 100 into decimals; remember hundreds are the second column to the right of the decimal point. So $\frac{1}{100}$ or 1% is 0.01 as a decimal (not 0.1).

15: 2D shape

Two-dimensional (2D) shapes are flat shapes that can be drawn on paper and have no depth. Those with straight sides only are called polygons.

We have special names for some shapes, such as for triangles and quadrilaterals.

If a triangle has 3 equal sides and equal angles it is called an **equilateral triangle**. If it has 2 equal sides it is an **isosceles triangle** and if it has no equal sides it is called a **scalene triangle**.

Get ready

Name each of these triangles.

1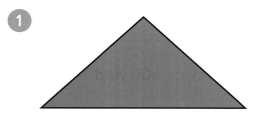

_____

2

_____

3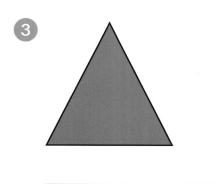

_____

4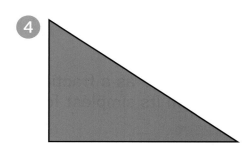

_____

5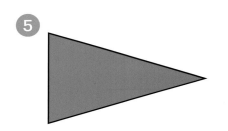

_____

6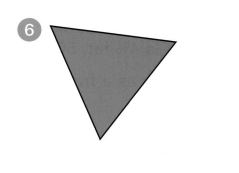

_____

Let's practise

7 Draw lines to match each quadrilateral with its most suitable name.

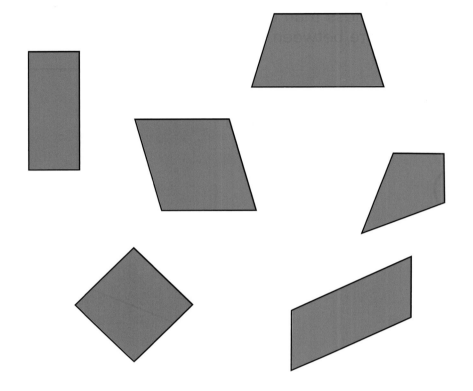

rhombus

square

rectangle

parallelogram

trapezium

kite

This pattern has been made by drawing different quadrilaterals. Draw a pattern using kites, squares, rectangles, rhombi, trapeziums and parallelograms.

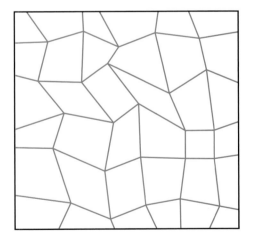

Teacher's tips

Many so-called shape 'names' are actually categories that can apply to many shapes (e.g. triangles, quadrilaterals) , some are true names that only apply to one specific shape (e.g. a square). Learn the difference!

16: Angles

An angle is an amount of turn and is measured in degrees. Angles less than a right angle are called **acute angles**. They are between 0° and 90°.

Angles larger than a right angle but less than two right angles are **obtuse angles**. They are between 90° and 180°.

Angles larger than a straight angle but less than a full turn are **reflex angles**. They are between 180° and 360°.

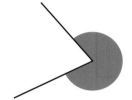

Get ready

Write whether each angle is acute, right, obtuse or reflex.

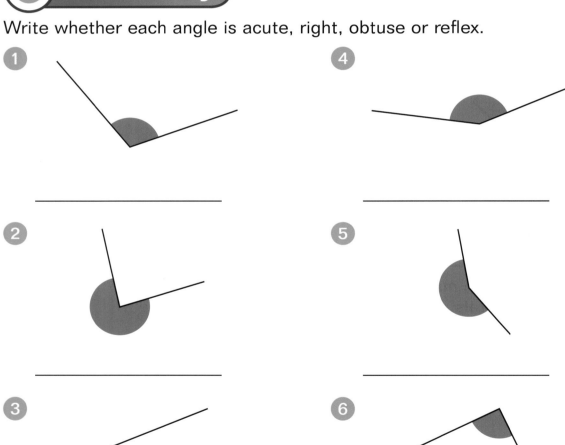

1

_____

2

_____

3

_____

4

_____

5

_____

6

_____

Let's practise

Angles about a point add up to 360°.

The size of each acute or obtuse angle is given. Work out the size of the reflex angle by subtracting from 360°.

7

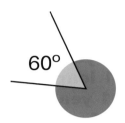

60°

_____

8

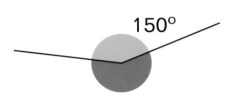

150°

_____

9

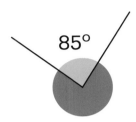

85°

_____

10

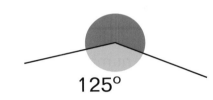

125°

_____

Have a go

Explore angles on a clock-face.

Through how many degrees does the minute hand of a clock turn between

- 10:05 and 10:50?
- 6:15 and 6:20?
- 1:25 and 2:15?

Teacher's tips

Learn the names of angles by remembering they're in alphabetical order: Acute (0–90), Obtuse (90–180) and Reflex (180–360). Think of everyday expressions like 'a 360 degree turn' (meaning a full turn about a point).

17: Measures

Make sure you know how many of one unit of measurement makes up another.

For length:
10 mm = 1 cm
100 cm = 1 m
1000 m = 1 km

For mass:
1000 g = 1 kg

For capacity:
1000 ml = 1 litre

For time:
60 seconds = 1 minute
60 minutes = 1 hour
24 hours = 1 day
7 days = 1 week
365 days = 1 year
366 days = 1 leap year
52 weeks = 1 year
12 months = 1 year

Get ready

Fill in the missing numbers.

1. _____ km = 8000 m

2. 1.5 kg = _____ g

3. _____ m = 250 cm

4. 10 kg = _____ g

5. 15 l = _____ ml

6. 1.5 cm = _____ mm

7. 28 l = _____ ml

8. 4.1 cm = _____ mm

9. _____ m = 1000 cm

10. 9.5 kg = _____ g

Let's practise

Fill in the missing numbers.

11 $\dfrac{1}{2}$ hour = _____ minutes

12 $\dfrac{1}{4}$ hour = _____ minutes

13 $\dfrac{3}{4}$ minute = _____ seconds

14 9 weeks = _____ days

15 5 years = _____ months

16 _____ minutes = 120 seconds

17 _____ weeks = 84 days

18 730 days = _____ years

Have a go

It is also useful to know about imperial units of measurement and their approximate metric equivalents.

Length 12 inches = 1 foot   3 feet = 1 yard   1760 yards = 1 mile

2.5 cm is about 1 inch   30 cm is about 1 foot

90 cm is about 1 yard   1.6 km is about 1 mile

Capacity 8 pints = 1 gallon

500 ml ($\dfrac{1}{2}$ litre) is about 1 pint   4.5 litres is about 1 gallon

Mass (weight) 16 ounces(oz) = 1 pound   14 pounds(lb) = 1 stone

25 g is about 1 ounce   400 g is about 1 pound

1 kg is about 2.2 pounds   6 kg is about 1 stone

Teacher's tips

Think of common objects that you know both metric and imperial measurements for to help estimate conversions – a standard ruler is 30cm which is also about 12 inches or 1 foot. A litre of milk is about 2 pints.

18: Area and perimeter

Area is the amount of surface that a shape covers. In a 2D shape (flat shape) it is the space inside the lines or within a boundary. We measure area in square units like square centimetres (cm^2) or square metres (m^2).

We can find the area of a rectangle by counting the number of squares or by **multiplying its length by its width**.

The area of this rectangle is $3\,cm \times 4\,cm = 12\,cm^2$.

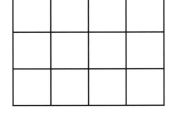

Write the area in cm^2 of each shape by counting squares.

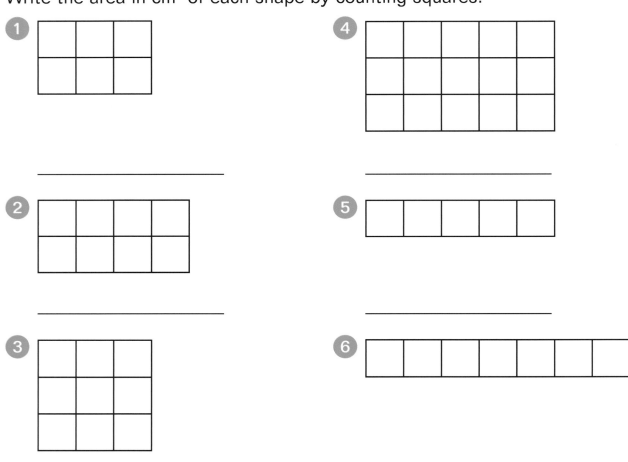

Let's practise

The perimeter of a shape is the distance all the way around the edge of the shape. It is measured in units of length such as cm or m.

7 For each of the shapes opposite, work out the perimeter in cm.

_____   _____

_____   _____

_____   _____

8 Write the area of each rectangle inside it.

7 cm

4 cm

8 cm

6 cm

9 Find the perimeter of each of the shapes above.

5 cm

6 cm

9 cm

4 cm

_____   _____

_____   _____

Have a go

On squared paper, draw as many rectangles as you can with an area of 24 cm².

19: Data handling

Pie charts use different sized parts of a circle to show information.

When looking at pie charts find out what the whole circle represents and look at how many equal parts the circle can be split into.

Then look at what fraction of the whole circle each section of the pie chart is.

 **Get ready**

This pie chart shows the results of the first **12 matches** of Manchester City's season.

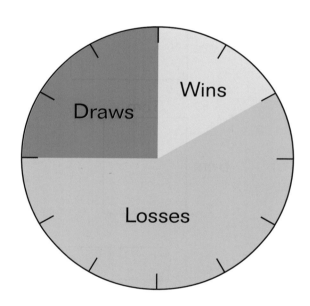

What fraction of the matches were:

1 draws? _____

2 wins? _____

3 losses? _____

How many of their 12 matches were:

4 draws? _____

5 wins? _____

6 losses? _____

Let's practise

This second pie chart shows the results of Manchester City's first **24 matches** of the season.

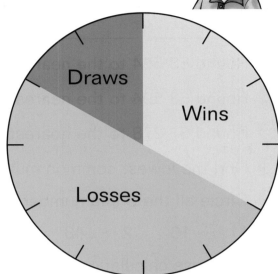

What fraction of these matches were:

7 draws? _____

8 wins? _____

9 losses? _____

How many of these 24 matches were:

10 draws? _____

11 wins? _____

12 losses? _____

13 After their 12th match, how many more matches did they win, draw and lose up and including to their 24th match?

_____

Have a go

Look in a newspaper or magazine for any pie charts. Try to work out what they are showing.

Teacher's tips

Pie charts are great for showing what proportion of the whole a particular data set is. As with any graph make sure you read the scales and labels carefully. Think about how you can also use your knowledge of angles to read pie charts.

How have I done?

1 Write this number in words. 433 568

_____

2 Continue this sequence

453 373, 463 373, 473 373, 483 373,

_____ , _____

3 Round 53 554 to the nearest 10. _____

4 Round 63 594 to the nearest 100. _____

5 Round 57 278 to the nearest 1000. _____

6 Find the lowest common multiple of 2, 3 and 5. _____

7 Circle all the prime numbers below.

    11   16   2   46   7   9   25   23   31

8 Do these calculations.

$$
\begin{array}{r}
36424 \\
+\,18653 \\
\hline
\end{array}
\qquad
\begin{array}{r}
36021 \\
-\,12339 \\
\hline
\end{array}
\qquad
724 \times 100 = \text{_____}
$$

$$
\begin{array}{r}
36853 \\
+\,47528 \\
\hline
\end{array}
\qquad
\begin{array}{r}
61545 \\
-\,14892 \\
\hline
\end{array}
\qquad
50\,600 \div 100 = \text{_____}
$$

9 Do these calculations.

$8 \times 7 =$ ____ $12 \times 11 =$ ____ $8 \times 8 =$ ____

$42 \div 6 =$ ____ $144 \div 12 =$ ____ $37 \div 6 =$ ____

10 Use a written method to find 425×36.

11 Use a written method to find $1735 \div 4$.

12 Order these fractions, smallest first. Change them so that they have the denominator 24.

$$
\frac{7}{12} \qquad \frac{5}{6} \qquad \frac{1}{2} \qquad \frac{3}{4} \qquad \frac{11}{24}
$$

_____

13 Write $\dfrac{13}{4}$ as a mixed number. _____

14 Write 75% as a decimal and as a fraction in its simplest form.

_____

15 Name this triangle.

_____

16 What is the size of this reflex angle?

17 A rectangle has sides of 8cm and 5 cm. Give its area and its perimeter.

Area = _____   Perimeter = _____

We hope you have learnt a lot and enjoyed your stay at Kids Club.

See you soon!

Problem Solving

- **Build understanding**
- **Use your maths to solve problems**

1: Place value

Place value questions often ask you to make up different numbers using different digits. The value of the digit changes depending on its 'place'.

When it's raining and we can't play outside we often play Maths card games. Knowing the values of digits helps me to win!

Get ready

1. Kim has five digit cards. They are 7, 4, 9, 5 and 2. He can only use each card once. What is the largest three-digit number he can make? Write your answer in words. _____

2. What is the smallest three-digit number Kim can make using the cards only once? Write your answer in words. _____

3. What is the largest three-digit number Kim can make if he can use a card a maximum of two times? Write your answer in words.

_____

4. Kim swaps all his cards for five new ones. They are 1, 6, 0, 8 and 3. What is the second largest three-digit number he can make using the cards just once? Write your answer in words. _____

_____

Let's practise

Let's make these problems a bit harder!

5 Kim now has a new set of digit cards. They are 3, 7, 4 and 8. What is the lowest four-digit number he can make using all the cards just once? Write your answer in numbers.

_____

6 Kim adds the card with the digit 5 to his hand. What is the second highest four-digit number he can make using any four of the five cards he has? Write your answer in numbers. _____

7 Kim now has all the digit cards. What is the smallest four-digit number he can make if he is allowed to use any three even digits and one odd digit? Write your answer in numbers. _____

8 Using all the cards, what is the highest four-digit number Kim can make if he uses any three odd digits and one even digit? Write your answer in numbers. _____

9 Place the digits 1, 3, 5, 7 and 9 in the boxes to get the highest answer. ☐☐ × ☐☐ + ☐ = _____

Have a go

Play this game with a friend.

Make two sets of 0 to 9 digit cards – one for each player.

You also need a timer or a stopwatch.

Shuffle and take four cards each.

Whoever makes the largest 3-digit number in ten seconds wins the round.

The first player to win an agreed number of rounds wins the game.

Teacher's tips

The position of a digit and its place value is the most important thing here – does the digit represent a number of units, tens, hundreds or even thousands?

2: Fractions

Fraction problems can be tricky because you are often dealing with words, fractions and whole numbers – lots to think about!

The Kids Club stayed in London for a weekend.

This trip to the city gave us lots of fraction problems to solve.

Get ready

1. When Alfie asked the coach driver if we were 'nearly there yet' the driver replied we were halfway. At that moment, we passed a sign saying London 128 miles. How far was our journey in total?

   _____

2. We spent three hours on a boat trip up and down the River Thames and one hour having a picnic. What fraction of the 24-hour day did we spend doing all this? _____

3. Charlie and Abbie booked a flight for us on the London Eye. It took 30 minutes for the Eye to go around once. One sixth of the way round I started to get frightened and wanted to get off! How long had I been on the London Eye before I got frightened?

   _____

4. At London Zoo I counted 50 snakes in the Reptile House. Three tenths of them were poisonous, the rest weren't. How many snakes were not poisonous? _____

Let's practise

We did a lot on our trip. Here are some more of our exploits.

5   Jamelia spent $\frac{3}{7}$ths of her total spending money on a giant inflatable Nelson's Column from a street seller. It cost her £18 and burst after an hour! How much spending money did Jamelia bring in total? _____

6   Kim tried to make one of the guards move who was guarding Buckingham Palace. He pulled funny faces and told his best jokes but still failed. He spent $\frac{2}{3}$ of an hour doing this while we ate ice cream. How many minutes did Kim try and make the guard move for? _____

7   An attendant at the waxworks museum told Megan that $\frac{2}{5}$ ths of their models were replaced each year. The museum had a total of 700 wax models. How many get replaced each year? _____

8   Alfie said that $\frac{7}{10}$ ths of his £30 spending money had been spent on sweets and drinks – the rest he had just wasted. How much did Alfie spend on sweets and drinks? _____

Have a go

If you sleep on average for 8 hours a night, what fraction of your life have you spent asleep? Work out some fractions for time spent on other things you do.

Teacher's tips

Think about what information is important in the question and what can be ignored; focus on the amounts and the actions. Write the problem down as a number sentence to help you solve it.

3: Decimals

Kids Club had a 'fun and games' day. It was brilliant, although Alfie is certain that someone jogged the table when he lost at Jenga. At the 'fun and games' day we had to think about some problems involving decimals.

Problems about decimals are often about measures or money. Don't forget which units you are working with.

Get ready

1. Kim fired a pea from a pea-shooter 8.6 m. Amina fired her pea 45 cm further than Kim. How far did Amina shoot her pea? Write your answer in metres. _____

2. Jamelia fired a foam air rocket a distance of 11.8 m. I fired mine 95 cm less far. How far in metres did my rocket travel?

   _____

3. Charlie and Abbie won the three-legged race in 18.5 seconds. Alfie and Kim were 3.5 seconds behind in second place. How many seconds did it take Alfie and Kim to complete the race?

   _____

4. Jamelia held the record for completing Charlie's 50-piece jigsaw of Elvis Presley in 56.3 seconds. Amina broke the record by 7 seconds! What is the time of the new record? _____

Let's practise

These events were great fun!

5   Kim tossed a Wellington boot 24.78 m. Alfie tossed his boot 22.57 m and Jamelia tossed her wellie 4.83 m further than Alfie. Who won and by how far? _____

6   Amina, Kim and I played a game of 'Hoop-shoot' – the person who scores 10 baskets with a basketball the fastest wins. Kim took 48.25 seconds. I was 5.12 seconds quicker than Kim but 3.83 seconds slower than Amina. What was Amina's time in seconds? _____

7   Each of us caught a snail and held a snail race. Here are the results after 10 minutes.

Jamelia's snail travelled 19.57 cm   Alfie's snail travelled 29.17 cm
My snail travelled 18.49 cm   Amina's snail travelled 3.04 cm
Kim's snail travelled 20.73 cm

What was the difference in distance travelled between the snail that came second and the snail that came fourth? _____

8   All five children made a tug of war team. This is how much each of them weighed.

Jamelia: 42.37 kg   Alfie: 41.97 kg   Amina: 36.28 kg
Kim: 40.75 kg   Megan: 37.86 kg

They tugged against Charlie and Abbie who together weighed 145.50 kg. Which was the heavier team and by how much?

Have a go

Give yourself an imaginary £500. Look through a mail order catalogue or one from a local store. 'Spend' the £500 on gifts for yourself and your family. Can you spend the £500 to the exact penny?

Teacher's tips

Convert each amount so that it is expressed the same way: if the question has values in metres and centimetres convert the metres to centimetres first. You can convert the answer back at the end.

4: Percentages

Percentage problems are sometimes about money. You might be asked to find the percentage of an amount or to work out the discount off a price.

The Kids Club have received a government grant for some new outdoor sports equipment – cool!

Charlie and Abbie took us to 'Lilly-Livers' the sports shop; there was a big sale on and we wanted to pick up some bargains.

Get ready

1. Jamelia thought we needed a new netball post. The old one had rusted and the net had rotted years ago. One was priced at £90. It had a '10% off' tag tied to it. How much would the netball post cost after the discount? _____

2. Amina told Charlie that a set of 12 footballs would cost 15% less if you bought a carry net for £5. The set of balls was priced at £30. How much would the set of balls and a net cost altogether?

   _____

3. I told the shopkeeper that because his tennis racket had lots of holes in it I wanted a 75% discount! The racket cost £40. How much did I offer to pay? _____

4. A crazy golf set cost £150, but one of the nine holes was broken and the windmill wouldn't go round, so it was on sale with 60% off. What was the price of the crazy golf set after the discount? _____

Let's practise

These are some more great deals we got.

5 Mountain bikes were on special offer. One was £79 with 10% off, one was £89 with 20% off and one was £99 with 30% off. Charlie and Abbie bought all three bikes. How much did they pay in total?

_____

6 The price of a climbing frame and tyre swing was £290 in the sale. When the sale ended the price would go up by 15%. How much would it cost once the sale had ended?

_____

7 A water-slide was on special offer because of a hose-pipe ban. You could buy one for 35% of its original price. Its price before the ban was £55. What was the price during the hose-pipe ban? _____

8 The grant for equipment was £1300. Charlie and Abbie spent 70% in May, 10% in June and 15% in July. How much did they have left to spend when Kids Club started again in September?

Have a go

If you put £1 in a saving account which paid 10% interest each year, how much would be in the account after 25 years? Remember to add the interest each year and then calculate the 10%. For example, after year 1 you would have £1.10. After year 2 you would have £1.21 (£1.10 plus the 10% which is 11p). Round to the nearest 1p, so for year 3 you would add 12p to make £1.33. Use a calculator to help you.

Teacher's tips

10% is the same as $\frac{1}{10}$, which is straightforward to calculate, so calculate larger percentages by breaking them down into lots of 10%. Remember 5% will be half of whatever 10% is.

5: Addition

Addition problems often involve adding three- or four-digit numbers. Mistakes can be made if you are not careful. Once you have decided which calculations you need to do, remember: estimate, calculate, then check.

Charlie bought an old and broken pinball machine from a fun-fair. He repaired it and it now stands proudly in the Kids Club – we love it!

Get ready

1. Jamelia played pinball with Alfie. Jamelia scored 487 points with her first ball, 274 with her second and the third ball went straight down the chute without scoring! How many points did Jamelia score with her three balls in total? _____

2. Alfie scored 692 with his first ball and got his score doubled when he hit the 'double trouble' bumper. His second ball scored just 25 points before he lost it between the flippers. How many points did Alfie score with the two balls in total? _____

3. Alfie did really well with his third ball. He hit lots of bumpers and targets and scored 894 points with a 977 bonus. How many points did Alfie score with his third ball in total? _____

4. How many points did Alfie and Jamelia score between them?

_____

Let's practise

We held a pinball tournament.
Here are the final scores.

PLAYER	FINAL SCORE
Jamelia	5829
Kim	6728
Alfie	6092
Megan	9241
Amina	2987
Charlie	4729
Abbie	8593

5   What is the total number of points scored by Charlie and Abbie?

_____

6   What is the sum of the points for the person who came first and the person who came third? _____

7   How many are Kim's and Jamelia's scores altogether? _____

8   What is the total of the two lowest scores? _____

9   How many points did the children score in total between them?

_____

Have a go

Challenge yourself to add up totals in your head. Look for numbers around you, at home, out shopping, in newspapers and on TV. Use 'rounding' to add big numbers mentally and you'll be surprised how accurate you can be.

Practise mental addition as often as possible.

Teacher's tips

Whichever method you choose for these calculations make sure you write down the working out in the margin or on another piece of paper. Estimate the answers by rounding the numbers; your answer should be close.

6: Subtraction

Subtraction problems can involve finding the difference between two-, three- or four-digit numbers. Estimating first will help you get these right. You can check your answers when you have finished.

We have been making a timeline for a display at Kids Club. When the children find out something interesting from books or from a TV programme they research it further, write a short article and mark it on the timeline. It's an on-going project.

Get ready

1. Kim found out about the First World War which ended in 1918. How long ago was that from this year? _____

2. Jamelia was interested in the artist Vincent Van Gogh. He died in 1890. How long is it since he died? _____

3. Megan did some research on Queen Victoria. She came to the throne in 1837 and died in 1901. How long ago is 1837? _____

4. Kim studied the life and work of the composer Mozart. He was a child prodigy and was born in 1756. How many years ago is that?

_____

Let's practise

Alfie has written a story about travelling back in time to see exciting events in history.

Here are some of the events in the story and some questions about the dates.

5   Alfie travelled back to 1666 and helped to put out the Great Fire of London. How many years back is that? _____

6   From 1666 he then went back to join King Henry V at the Battle of Agincourt in 1415. How many years further back was that from the Great Fire of London? _____

7   Alfie's next adventure was leaving Agincourt to go back in time to meet the last Viking king in England, Eric Bloodaxe, in 954. How many years before Agincourt was that? _____

8   Alfie had heard about the beauty of the Egyptian Queen Cleopatra so in his story he travelled back to 51 BC to see for himself. How long before 954 is that? Be careful here! _____

9   Finally, Alfie returned to the present day but decided on one last trip in his time machine. He returned to Ancient Egypt and helped build the Great Pyramid in 2593 BC. How many years ago is that from today?

_____

Have a go

Using books and the Internet, research five events in history which interest you.

How many years before you were born did they occur?

Teacher's tips

Think of these timeline jumps as subtraction calculations – think about which number you need to start with and which you need to subtract from it.

7: Multiplication

Multiplication problems are often 'story' problems about measures or money. Make sure you identify the numbers to multiply and include the units. Remember that if you are asked to find the product of two numbers it means you must multiply them.

The children have been growing fruit and vegetables in an allotment at the back of the Kids Club. It is harvest time!

Get ready

1. Jamelia has grown eight strawberry plants on the allotment. She picked 37 strawberries off each plant to make some jam. How many strawberries did Jamelia pick altogether? _____

2. Kim chose to grow raspberry plants. These have been very successful. From nine plants, Kim picked 45 raspberries off each one. How many raspberries did Kim pick altogether? _____

3. Jamelia's jam was sold to parents after school. Each pot cost £1.25. Jamelia made 20 pots. She kept three for herself and family and sold the rest. How much did she get for her jam in total? _____

4. Kim eventually picked 4.3 kg of raspberries. He and his Mum made 35 litres of raspberry cordial. They sold the cordial for 95p a litre after keeping 8 litres for themselves. How much did they make in total from selling the cordial? _____

Let's practise

These are a bit more difficult but give them a go.

5 Alfie grew potatoes and Megan grew leeks. They decided to make some leek and potato soup. It was so good; the school served it for lunch! The school paid Alfie and Megan 87p per litre. Alfie and Megan made 48 litres of soup. How much were they paid? _____

6 Amina loves runner beans so she grew those. Each time she picked beans off the plant some more grew in their place. From 16 bean plants, Amina picked 27 beans off each one three times. How many beans did she pick altogether? _____

7 Abbie and I both grew grapevines. From 23 vines we grew an average of 376 grapes on each. What is the number of grapes grown in total?

_____

8 We made wine from our grapes. It was quite a good year! We managed to sell 56 bottles to a local restaurant for £1.85 per bottle. How much did the restaurant give us for the wine? _____

Have a go

Count the number of beats your heart makes in a minute. How many times would your heart beat in an hour?

What is the product of the number of times your heart beats in an hour and the number of hours in a day? (The number of beats will vary depending on how active you are.)

Teacher's tips

Underline the important information in the story – the quantities and the actions – and write them as numbers and maths symbols to create a number sentence with '?' as the missing information you need to calculate.

8: Division

Always read division questions carefully and work out which number needs to be divided. Usually you have to find how many times the smaller number 'fits into' the bigger number.

The Kids Club support the local Premiership football team who often give cheap tickets to families, schools and clubs like ours. It can still be expensive though, so we try to save up.

Get ready

1 There are 288 half-price tickets given equally to 12 different schools. How many tickets does each school receive? _____

2 The next allocation is for 232 tickets to the big cup match. These are given equally to eight after-school clubs like ours – hooray! How many tickets does each after-school club receive? _____

3 The football club then gives away 432 tickets for the quarter-final of the cup. They could either be shared between the 12 schools, or between the 8 after-school clubs. Who would receive more tickets, a school or an after-school club? How many more? _____

4 For the semi-final of the cup, 520 pupils, parents and children from after-school members are going. It promises to be a great day! The football club have donated a mini-bus to get people to the ground. Unfortunately, it can only take 20 people at a time for the 10-minute round trip. How long would it take to bus everyone to the ground?

_____

Let's practise

I'm glad I didn't hang around for the mini-bus; we all walked to the game.

5 Twelve football-mad parents paid a total of £960 for front row seats at the match and a chance to meet the players in the players' lounge afterwards. How much did they pay equally between them? _____

6 Sixteen other football-mad parents paid a total of £720 for autographed footballs from the players! How much did each parent pay for an autographed ball? _____

7 The stadium can hold 45 000 people. How many mini-bus loads of 20 people is that? _____

8 The restaurants and bars inside the stadium made £84 000. If the average amount spent by a customer was £5, how many customers used the bars and restaurants? _____

9 The game was a sell-out and raised a total of £1 125 000 from ticket sales alone (45 000 tickets). What was the average cost of a ticket to the game? (You can use a calculator but first try without.)

_____

Have a go

The new Wembley Stadium can hold 90 000 people. If 50% of the seats were given to corporate hospitality, 50% of the remainder were given to season ticket holders, 50% of the remainder given to football club members and 50% of the rest given to officials and staff, how many tickets would be left to sell to the general public?

Teacher's tips

Estimate the answer first by rounding up quantities to the nearest 10 or hundred. Read the question carefully – is it a division or multiplication problem? Highlight the key information to form the calculation. Check your answer against your estimate.

9: Money

These problems involve all four operations: addition, subtraction, multiplication and division. Most of them are decimal problems as well, so watch the decimal points!

Get ready

1 I earn £12 per week pocket money by doing jobs around the house. I want to save all my earnings for 15 weeks for when we go on holiday. How much will I have if I do save for 15 weeks? _____

2 Fifteen weeks is quite a long time without spending any money! If I save £9 per week and spend the rest, how much will I have saved after 13 weeks? _____

3 For the two weeks before our holiday I will work extra hard and deliver papers for the newsagent. I will get paid £38 for the two weeks doing the paper round.
How much will I be able to take on holiday if I take my 13 weeks' worth of savings and all my paper round earnings? _____

4 Just before we went away, I bought myself a new swimming costume with my holiday money for £19.99. My Dad gave me £10 towards it. How much of my money did I have left to spend? _____

Let's practise

Last week I had rather a bad accident. My new scooter hit the kerb and smashed the windscreen of our neighbour's car! The damage cost £140. My Dad paid for it but I'm going to have to pay him back …

5 The £140 is to be paid back at a rate of £1 per day. How many weeks is that in total? _____

6 I can earn 25p for ironing my Dad's shirts and 35p for ironing a pair of trousers. If I iron 16 shirts and 4 pairs of trousers, how much will I still have to pay? _____

7 My Mum felt sorry for me. She said she would give me all the coins in her jar if I vacuumed and dusted the entire house. It was not a good deal. There were 195 pennies, 286 2p coins, 46 5p coins and 53 10p coins. How much did I collect from the jar? _____

8 After the ironing and cleaning, how much was left to pay of the £140?

_____

9 I eventually paid the money back to Dad. He was so pleased with me for working so hard, that he took me and my friends out for an Indian meal and a trip to the cinema! This is what he spent:
Tickets – £36.50   Curries and rice – £47.31   Sweets – £13.96
Popcorn – £14.28   Drinks and desserts – £27.95
How much did Dad spend in total? _____

Have a go

Think about ways you could earn some money. Are there any jobs or errands you could do for friends and family? Add up what you could earn. Are there any unwanted toys to sell? Is there anything you want to save up for? Learning to handle money well is a useful skill.

Teacher's tips

Money problems are just the same as other calculations because money uses the decimal system – just mind the units and decimal point to make sure you calculate the correct values.

Time problems often ask you to work out the difference between two times.

This is what I did on Saturday with Jamelia. It was her turn to sleep over at my house.

Get ready

1 Jamelia called round on Saturday morning at 9.30 a.m. We left at 10.55 p.m. to catch the bus into town. How long was it from when Jamelia came round to when we left to catch the bus?

_____

2 We had lunch at a sandwich bar at 12.10 p.m. We were there for an hour and a half! What time did we leave the sandwich bar?

_____

3 We went to the cinema to see the new film which started at 2.45 p.m. It said in the magazine review that the film lasted one hour and fifty minutes, so what time did the film end? _____

4 My Mum picked us up after the film. Jamelia stayed the night and we were up chatting until 12.15 a.m! Dad got us out of bed in the morning at 8.45 a.m. How many hours sleep did we get? _____

Let's practise

Jamelia and I helped my Mum and Dad cook Sunday lunch. We drew up a table for cooking times but got it all wrong and burnt the joint!

Fill in this table so the cooking times are correct.

	KILOGRAMS/ COOKING TIMES	1KG	1.5KG	2KG	2.5KG	3KG	3.5KG
5	Roast chicken 40 mins per kilo + 20 mins						
6	Nut roast loaf 50 mins per kilo + 25 mins						
7	Roast pork 60 mins per kilo+ 25 mins						
8	Frozen vegetable lasagne 80 mins per kilo + 30 mins						

9   If we put a 2.5 kg frozen vegetable lasagne in the oven at 10.12 a.m., at what time would it be ready? _____

Have a go

Investigate different cooking times for different foods.

Which take longest to cook? Which ones can be cooked in seconds?

Look in recipe books and on the Internet.

Make up some Maths questions about your findings for a friend to answer.

Teacher's tips

Remember there are 60 minutes in an hour (not 100) so even though time is written the same way as decimal numbers, you can't calculate time using the same methods.

Charlie is playing cricket for the local team. We are all going to the game to watch him. Jamelia and Kim have made a picnic and Abbie has made the tea for the players – more sandwiches and cakes than I've ever seen!

Measures problems are about adding, subtracting, dividing and multiplying weights, lengths and capacities. Lots of things to think about!

Get ready

1. The weight of a cricket ball is 156 g. What is the weight of the six cricket balls in a box? _____

2. The width of the cricket pitch is 95 m. The umpire asks for the width to be increased by 50 cm. How wide is the pitch now in metres?

   _____

3. Charlie is batting and hits the ball 36 m to score one run. The second time he hits it, the ball goes two and a half times further. How far did Charlie hit the ball on his second hit? _____

4. Charlie hits a high shot over the bowler's head. The ball travels 45 m to a fielder who fumbles the catch and knocks the ball a further 16 m. How many centimetres has the ball travelled? _____

Let's practise

Charlie scored 56 runs! Now his team are fielding.

5   Charlie is bowling. His run up to bowl is 15.75 m. Charlie wants to bowl faster so he increases his run up by 575 cm. How long is his run up now in metres? _____

6   Kim lays out the picnic. He made 1.65 litres of ginger ale to share between six people. If it is shared equally, how many millilitres can each person have? _____

7   Jamelia cooked 150 cocktail sausages. They weighed 1.5 kg. Only $\frac{3}{5}$ths were eaten. How many sausages were left and how much did they weigh? _____

8   At the tea break, two teams of 12 players and the two umpires each eat 450 g of sandwiches and 375 g of cakes. How many kilograms of food are eaten by the players and umpires? _____

9   After the game, the 24 players and two umpires each drink 330 ml of shandy. There is 3.5 litres of shandy left. How many litres of shandy were made altogether? _____

Have a go

Cooking is the best way to learn about measures. Following recipes is like solving problems with measures. With the help of an adult, get an apron on and start cooking!

Teacher's tips

Make sure you know how many centimetres are in a metre, grams in a kilogram, and millilitres in a litre before you tackle measurement problems. Write them on a sheet at home to help.

Today is a rainy day at Kids Club. Charlie and Abbie have set us some number puzzles to keep us busy. Have a go at them yourself.

Number puzzles can be great fun but you need to think clearly to get them right.

Solve them by taking the calculations step-by-step and picturing the numbers in your head. What are you being asked to do?

Get ready

1. Abbie is thinking of a three-digit number. It is less than 200, can be divided exactly by 10 and the sum of the three digits is 7. What number is Abbie thinking of? _____

2. Which two numbers have a one-digit answer when multiplied and a two-digit answer when added? _____ _____

3. The ages of Gertie and Bertie add up to 55. Gertie's age is Bertie's age reversed. How old are Gertie and Bertie? _____ _____

4. There are 100 houses in Acacia Avenue. Sissy the sign-writer is ordered to number the houses from 1 to 100. How many '7s' will she need? _____

Let's practise

These are a bit harder. Give them your best shot!

5 All of Charlie's underpants are red except two.
All of Charlie's underpants are blue except two.
All of his underpants are pink except two.
How many pairs of underpants does Charlie
have? _____

6 Megan opened her reading book and found that the sum of the facing
pages was 245. What pages did she open the book to?

_____ _____

7 I have three digits and I'm less than 130. I can be divided exactly by 3
and 8. What am I? _____

8 Amina is thinking of a three-digit number. The hundreds digit is 3 times
more than the units digit. The sum of the three digits is 4. What
number is Amina thinking of? _____

9 Jamelia opened her piggy bank and found she had the same number of
10p, 20p and 50p coins which totalled £25.60. How many coins did she
have in the piggy bank? _____

Have a go

Sudoku puzzles are very popular but they are more to do with logic than
numbers. Look for some in newspapers or magazines and see if you can do
them.

Teacher's tips

Puzzles are much easier to solve if you can translate the problem into a number
sentence. Think about the clues in the question, and focus on the quantities and
the actions.

Pattern questions might ask you to find the '*n*th' number in a pattern or to work out how many numbers are in the pattern.

We have been studying the Ancient Greeks at school. They started the Olympic Games in 776 BC but the Olympics we see today began in 1896. They happen in a pattern – every four years.

Get ready

Fill in the missing years for these modern Olympic Games.

1 Munich 1972, Montreal 1976, Moscow _____, Los Angeles _____, Seoul 1988

2 London _____, Helsinki 1952, Melbourne 1956, Rome _____, Tokyo 1964

3 The London Olympics will be in 2012. When will the next three Olympics be held after then? _____

4 Since 1896, three Olympics have been cancelled because of war. How many games, including 1896, had there been by the end of 2004? _____

Let's practise

Halley's Comet is a comet that can be seen from Earth very rarely. Abbie set up a telescope to study the night sky. I wonder if she'll be able to see it?

5 Halley's Comet was last seen in 1986. The time before, it was seen in 1910 and the time before that was 1834. Would Abbie be able to see Halley's Comet if she viewed the sky for the next 4 years? Explain your answer. _____

_____

6 Halley's Comet appeared just before the Battle of Hastings in 1066. It was seen as an omen of doom! When were its next three appearances? _____

7 How many appearances of Halley's Comet can we expect in the next 1000 years? _____

8 The comet Swift–Tuttle was last seen in 1992. It will next be seen in 2127. When will the next two sightings be after that? _____

9 The comet Denning–Fujikawa was discovered in 1881. It can be seen every nine years. It was last seen in 2007. How many times has this comet been seen since its discovery and its last appearance?

_____

Have a go

Football is said to have been invented in Tudor times. Imagine if Elizabeth I had started the World Cup in 1588! If it was held every 8 years, how many 'World Cups' would there have been since 1588 up to the year 2000? (No breaks for wars!)

Teacher's tips

Work out the sequence by calculating what the change is between the numbers in the sequence that you are given, then go back and apply the same change to find the missing number.

The children at Kids Club have been making and drawing shapes for a display. See if you can identify what they have drawn.

These questions might ask you to add shapes together and then work out what the new shape is. Some are quiz-type questions where you might have some clues to solve.

Get ready

1   Megan has drawn an arrow shape. It has three sides and two of the sides are the same length. What is the name of the shape that Megan has drawn? _____

2   Alfie draws a star with six points. Each of the six points is the same distance apart. He then joins the points next to each other with straight lines. What is the name of the shape that Alfie has drawn?

_____

3   Amina slides an equilateral triangle next to a square. The sides are lined up exactly. What is the name of the new shape? _____

4   Kim slides two equilateral triangles together so the sides are lined up exactly. What is the name of the new shape? _____

Let's practise

These are a bit harder. Drawing them on a piece of paper might help.

5   Charlie takes a hexagon and adds an equilateral triangle on each of the sides. The triangles fit exactly. How many sides does this new shape have? _____

6   Abbie puts three equilateral triangles together to form a new shape; the name of it sounds like it belongs in the circus! What is the name of Abbie's shape? _____

7   Abbie adds a fourth equilateral triangle to her new shape. Which two shapes can she make?

_____

8   What do the prefixes 'quad', 'tri' and 'hex' stand for? _____

_____

9   I made a beautiful flower pattern for our display. I took a regular octagon and placed a square on each of the octagon's sides. They fitted exactly. How many sides does this 'flower shape' have?

_____

Have a go

Make sure you know all the names of the 2D shapes up to ten sides. Learn how to spell them correctly as well! If all their sides are the same length, they are 'regular polygons'. If their sides are different lengths they are 'irregular polygons'.

Teacher's tips

As well as shape names, learn what other terms like 'equilateral' and 'right-angle' mean. To help you remember shape names think of everyday objects with the same prefixes, like tricycle, octopus and quad-bikes!

Alfie was getting a box of 3D shapes down from the cupboard. Unfortunately he stood on a stray sphere and dropped the lot! Some of the cuboids were broken.

Alfie was okay but he did hurt his bottom on a square-based pyramid – ouch!

As you should know, 3D shapes are solid shapes. It is particularly useful to be able to picture 3D shapes in your head and 'see round them'. A good imagination is useful in Maths.

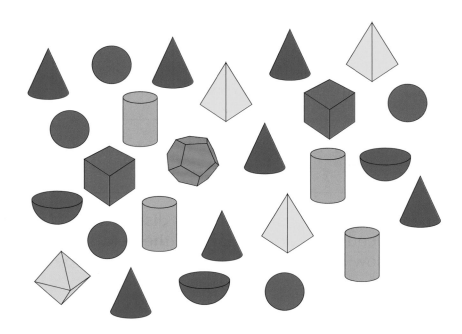

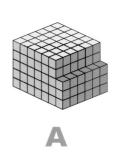

A

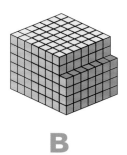

B

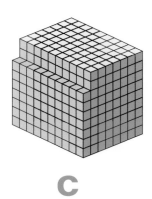

C

Let's practise

Answer these questions about the pictures on the opposite page.

1 How many cylinders can you see?

_____

2 How many hemispheres are there?

_____

3 Count the number of cones. _____

4 How many square-based pyramids are there? _____

5 What colour is the octahedron? _____

6 What colour is the dodecahedron? _____

7 If the damaged shapes were repaired there would be five cubes. True or false? _____

8 How many blocks are needed to repair shape A so it is a complete cuboid? _____

9 How many blocks are needed to repair shape B so it is a complete cuboid? _____

10 How many blocks are needed to repair shape C so it is a complete cuboid? _____

Have a go

Learn all the names of the 3D shapes up to the dodecahedron and their spellings.

It may come in useful for any tests you take.

Teacher's tips

To help you learn 3D shape names and their properties, find objects at home that are different shapes, or make your own, and try labelling them. Your school may have a set you could ask your teacher to put on display.

Position and direction questions may ask you to look at maps and grid references. You may also need to find the coordinates of different landmarks.

This is a map of 'Queasy Rider' Amusement Park that is close by. It's great to visit!

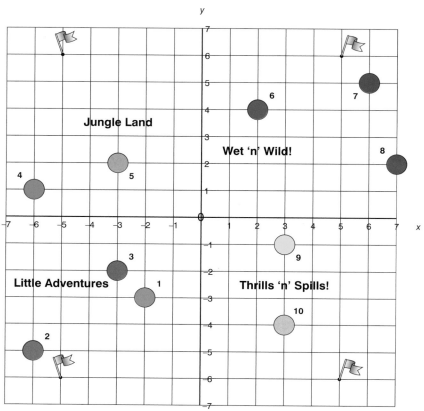

Queasy Rider Amusement Park

KEY:

1 = Tea-Cup Ride
2 = Soft Play Area
3 = Sandpit
4 = Big Cat World
5 = Penguin Pool

6 = Pirate Waterslide
7 = Log Flume
8 = Vertical Splash!
9 = Big Hoop Coaster
10 = Queasy Rider Coaster

= Flag

1. In which zone would you find the Log Flume?
   _____

2. What are the coordinates of the Tea-Cup Ride? _____

3. Write down the coordinates of the Soft Play Area. _____

4. If you were at (−3, −2) where would you be? _____

5. What would you be looking at if you were at (−3, 2)? _____

6. Give the coordinates for Big Cat World. _____

7. What would you be doing at (7, 2)? _____

8. Where exactly would you find the Pirate Waterslide? _____

9. A visitor tells you the Queasy Rider is at (−4, 3). Are they correct? Explain your answer. _____

   _____

10. Give the coordinates of the four Queasy Rider Flags. _____

    _____

Have a go

Sketch a map of your garden or the local park. Draw a grid and label the coordinates over the sketch in pencil. Note down the coordinates of features and landmarks in the garden or park. Write three questions you could ask a friend about your map.

Teacher's tips

The first number is always the place on the x-axis (along/horizontal), the second is the place on the y-axis (up/vertical). Remember: across, then up.

Questions about handling data will ask you to look at a graph, chart or table and analyse the data. Sometimes you will have to transfer data from a table.

Here is a frequency chart showing how I lost at my favourite console game – 'Space Monkeys Meet the Killer Kittens'.

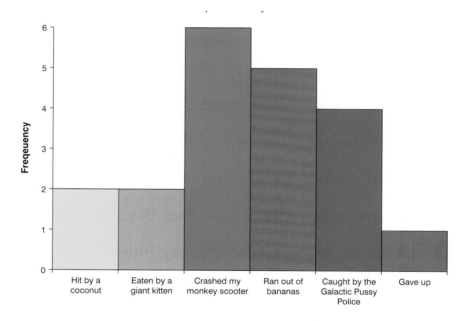

Get ready

1. How many times did Alfie run out of bananas? _____

2. What was the most common way Alfie lost a game? _____

3. How many games in total did Alfie lose by being eaten and getting caught? _____

4. How many games did Alfie play altogether? _____

Let's practise

As part of a Kids Club project about the history of Rock'n'Roll, we did the following survey.

'Which age group of fans think The Beatles were the most successful band ever?'

5 Which age group of fans had the least responses?

_____

6 Which age group answered six times in the survey?

_____

7 How many people in the 41–50 age group said The Beatles were the most successful band? _____

8 How many people over 30 said The Beatles were the most successful?

_____

9 How many people answered the survey altogether? _____

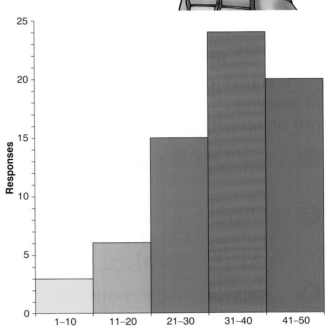

Have a go

If this graph was about whether your favourite, newest band is the most successful of all time, how do you think it would look? Think about what the different age groups might say. Run the survey and draw the graph!

Teacher's tips

Always look very carefully at the scales on a graph; graphs that look similar can show very different data if the scales are different (you might think about when people would want to do this deliberately!).

Here is a chance to see how well you are able to solve problems in a number of areas in Maths. Read the questions carefully and think about what you are being asked to do.

1. Kim has the digit cards 4, 8, 2 and 9. What is the second largest number he can make using his cards? (1 mark) _____

2. Jamelia had 360 tracks on her CDs. She put $\frac{5}{6}$ths of the tracks onto her new MP3 player. How many tracks did Jamelia put onto her MP3 player? (1 mark) _____

3. Alfie and Megan went fishing. Alfie caught a carp which was 42.8 cm long. Megan caught an eel which was 3.9 cm shorter. How long was the eel? (1 mark) _____

4. Charlie bought himself a new cricket bat in a sale. It was priced at £65 but was reduced by 20%. What was the price of the bat after the reduction? (1 mark) _____

5. Amina scored 4823 on the pinball machine and Jamelia scored 5582 more. How many points did Jamelia score in total? (1 mark) _____

6. The first manned balloon flight was in 1783. The first man to land on the Moon did so in 1969. What is the difference in years of these two aeronautical feats? (1 mark) _____

7. Abbie sold 89 homemade cakes at 75p each. How much did she make altogether? (1 mark) _____

8   Kim had a collection of stickers. He had 288 spares to share equally between 16 people. How many did they each receive? (1 mark)

_____

9   Abbie and Charlie went to a restaurant. They had 2 × lasagne at £4.85 each and 2 × fruit salad at £2.70 each. How much was the bill? (2 marks) _____

10   Amina read her book from 7.45 p.m. until 9.07 p.m. How many minutes did Amina read her book for? (1 mark) _____

11   On a sponsored walk, Alfie walked 4.8 km, Kim walked 3 km, Megan hurt her foot and walked 0.25 km, Jamelia walked 6.3 km and Amina walked 6.8 km. What was the total distance walked by all the children? (1 mark) _____

12   What am I? I have three digits, I am a prime number less than 200 and the sum of my digits is 14. (1 mark) _____

13   The first Rugby World Cup was held in 1987. It takes place every four years. When was the fifth Rugby World Cup held? (1 mark)

_____

14   What am I? I have three sides which are all unequal in length. (1 mark)

_____ _____

15   What am I? I have two faces yet I'm a 3D shape. (1 mark)

_____ _____

16   Charlie is facing east and makes a 270° turn clockwise. He then makes a 90° turn anti-clockwise. In which direction is he facing? (1 mark)

_____

Total marks $\frac{}{17}$

Teacher's tips

Read the questions carefully, make sure you note the units and express answers using the correct units. Make as many notes as you need in the margin or on another piece of paper. Check your work using the inverse operation.

Maths tools

These may help you with some of the questions in this book.

1 WHOLE									

| $\frac{1}{2}$ | | | | | $\frac{1}{2}$ | | | | |

| $\frac{1}{3}$ | | | $\frac{1}{3}$ | | | $\frac{1}{3}$ | | | |

| $\frac{1}{4}$ | | $\frac{1}{4}$ | | $\frac{1}{4}$ | | $\frac{1}{4}$ | | | |

| $\frac{1}{5}$ | $\frac{1}{5}$ | $\frac{1}{5}$ | $\frac{1}{5}$ | $\frac{1}{5}$ |

| $\frac{1}{6}$ | $\frac{1}{6}$ | $\frac{1}{6}$ | $\frac{1}{6}$ | $\frac{1}{6}$ | $\frac{1}{6}$ |

| $\frac{1}{7}$ | $\frac{1}{7}$ | $\frac{1}{7}$ | $\frac{1}{7}$ | $\frac{1}{7}$ | $\frac{1}{7}$ | $\frac{1}{7}$ |

| $\frac{1}{8}$ | $\frac{1}{8}$ | $\frac{1}{8}$ | $\frac{1}{8}$ | $\frac{1}{8}$ | $\frac{1}{8}$ | $\frac{1}{8}$ | $\frac{1}{8}$ |

| $\frac{1}{9}$ | $\frac{1}{9}$ | $\frac{1}{9}$ | $\frac{1}{9}$ | $\frac{1}{9}$ | $\frac{1}{9}$ | $\frac{1}{9}$ | $\frac{1}{9}$ | $\frac{1}{9}$ |

| $\frac{1}{10}$ | $\frac{1}{10}$ | $\frac{1}{10}$ | $\frac{1}{10}$ | $\frac{1}{10}$ | $\frac{1}{10}$ | $\frac{1}{10}$ | $\frac{1}{10}$ | $\frac{1}{10}$ | $\frac{1}{10}$ |

Fraction, decimal and percentage equivalents

$\frac{1}{2} = 0.50 = 50\%$

$\frac{1}{4} = 0.25 = 25\%$

$\frac{3}{4} = 0.75 = 75\%$

$\frac{1}{10} = 0.10 = 10\%$

$\frac{1}{100} = 0.01 = 1\%$

$\frac{1}{3} = 0.333 = 33.33\%$

1 whole = 1.0 = 100%
(approximately)

$\frac{1}{3} = 0.33 = 33\%$ (approximately)

$\frac{2}{3} = 0.66 = 66\%$ (approximately)

Use this hundred square to help you with your calculations.

1	2	3	4	5	6	7	8	9	10
11	12	13	14	15	16	17	18	19	20
21	22	23	24	25	26	27	28	29	30
31	32	33	34	35	36	37	38	39	40
41	42	43	44	45	46	47	48	49	50
51	52	53	54	55	56	57	58	59	60
61	62	63	64	65	66	67	68	69	70
71	72	73	74	75	76	77	78	79	80
81	82	83	84	85	86	87	88	89	90
91	92	93	94	95	96	97	98	99	100

Multiplication tables

1 x 1 = 1	2 x 1 = 2	3 x 1 = 3	4 x 1 = 4	5 x 1 = 5	6 x 1 = 6
1 x 2 = 2	2 x 2 = 4	3 x 2 = 6	4 x 2 = 8	5 x 2 = 10	6 x 2 = 12
1 x 3 = 3	2 x 3 = 6	3 x 3 = 9	4 x 3 = 12	5 x 3 = 15	6 x 3 = 18
1 x 4 = 4	2 x 4 = 8	3 x 4 = 12	4 x 4 = 16	5 x 4 = 20	6 x 4 = 24
1 x 5 = 5	2 x 5 = 10	3 x 5 = 15	4 x 5 = 20	5 x 5 = 25	6 x 5 = 30
1 x 6 = 6	2 x 6 = 12	3 x 6 = 18	4 x 6 = 24	5 x 6 = 30	6 x 6 = 36
1 x 7 = 7	2 x 7 = 14	3 x 7 = 21	4 x 7 = 28	5 x 7 = 35	6 x 7 = 42
1 x 8 = 8	2 x 8 = 16	3 x 8 = 24	4 x 8 = 32	5 x 8 = 40	6 x 8 = 48
1 x 9 = 9	2 x 9 = 18	3 x 9 = 27	4 x 9 = 36	5 x 9 = 45	6 x 9 = 54
1 x 10 = 10	2 x 10 = 20	3 x 10 = 30	4 x 10 = 40	5 x 10 = 50	6 x 10 = 60
1 x 11 = 11	2 x 11 = 22	3 x 11 = 33	4 x 11 = 44	5 x 11 = 55	6 x 11 = 66
1 x 12 = 12	2 x 12 = 24	3 x 12 = 36	4 x 12 = 48	5 x 12 = 60	6 x 12 = 72

7 x 1 = 7	8 x 1 = 8	9 x 1 = 9	10 x 1 = 10	11 x 1 = 11	12 x 1 = 12
7 x 2 = 14	8 x 2 = 16	9 x 2 = 18	10 x 2 = 20	11 x 2 = 22	12 x 2 = 24
7 x 3 = 21	8 x 3 = 24	9 x 3 = 27	10 x 3 = 30	11 x 3 = 33	12 x 3 = 36
7 x 4 = 28	8 x 4 = 32	9 x 4 = 36	10 x 4 = 40	11 x 4 = 44	12 x 4 = 48
7 x 5 = 35	8 x 5 = 40	9 x 5 = 45	10 x 5 = 50	11 x 5 = 55	12 x 5 = 60
7 x 6 = 42	8 x 6 = 48	9 x 6 = 54	10 x 6 = 60	11 x 6 = 66	12 x 6 = 72
7 x 7 = 49	8 x 7 = 56	9 x 7 = 63	10 x 7 = 70	11 x 7 = 77	12 x 7 = 84
7 x 8 = 56	8 x 8 = 64	9 x 8 = 72	10 x 8 = 80	11 x 8 = 88	12 x 8 = 96
7 x 9 = 63	8 x 9 = 72	9 x 9 = 81	10 x 9 = 90	11 x 9 = 99	12 x 9 = 108
7 x 10 = 70	8 x 10 = 80	9 x 10 = 90	10 x 10 = 100	11 x 10 = 110	12 x 10 = 120
7 x 11 = 77	8 x 11 = 88	9 x 11 = 99	10 x 11 = 110	11 x 11 = 121	12 x 11 = 132
7 x 12 = 84	8 x 12 = 96	9 x 12 = 108	10 x 12 = 120	11 x 12 = 132	12 x 12 = 144

Number line from –20 to +20

-20   -10   0   10   20

Glossary

These are words you may come across when problem solving at home or at school. Many Maths questions come in the form of 'word problems' so it's really important that you understand what you are being asked to do! Always read the question and then read it again to help your understanding. When you arrive at an answer, does it look sensible? If not, re-read the question and check your calculations.

Answer – The solution to a problem. Usually what you are trying to find out!

Calculate – To 'work out' mathematically.

Calculation – If you are asked to 'show your calculations' then write down the 'working out' that you did to get your answer.

Correct – The right answer; or you can correct your mistakes by changing wrong answers to right ones.

Equation – A statement that shows two mathematical expressions are equal. (Using the sign =) For example, 10 + 5 = 15.

Jotting – Brief or short notes that you might make in your book or on paper.

Mental calculation – 'Working out' that you do in your head. When solving problems you should first try to do them in your head. If they are too hard, use a written method. If they are still too hard then use a calculator.

Method – A way of doing something. You may be asked to 'explain your method'. This means write down how you tackled the problem.

Number sentence – E.g. 46 – 32 = 14 is a number sentence. So is (5 x 3) + 69 – 11 = 73.

Operation – The four operations you need to know are addition, subtraction, multiplication and division. You may be asked 'Which operation did you use?'

Symbol – Maths uses lots of symbols. +, –, x and ÷ are the symbols for the four operations. Others are = for equals, > for greater than and < for less than.

Strategies for Solving Problems

At the beginning –

- How are you going to tackle the problem?
- What information do you have?
- Will you need any equipment?
- What method are you going to use?
- Can you predict or estimate the answer?

During the problem –

- Can you explain to yourself what you have done so far?
- Could there be a quicker way to do this?
- Can you see a pattern or a rule?
- Is there another method that would have worked?
- How will you show your results?

Stuck? –

- What did you do last time? What is different this time?
- Is there something you already know that might help?
- Can you put things in order?
- Would drawing a picture/graph/table/diagram help?
- Have you worked through the problem step-by-step in a logical way?

Problem solved! –

- How did you get your answer?
- Have you checked your answer?
- Does your answer make sense?
- If you were doing it again, what would you do differently?
- What have you learned or found out today?

Answers

UNIT 1

Ancient: very old; **Appreciate**: admire; **Atmosphere**: air; **Committee**: group of people; **Correspond**: send letters; **Curious**: strange; **Definite**: certain; **Especially**: particularly; **Genuine**: real; **Interrupt**: break into; **Marvellous**: amazing; **Mosquito**: biting insect; **Nuisance**: interfering problem; **Persevere**: keep going; **Succeed**: do well; **Suggest**: contribute an idea; **Theatre**: place where plays are put on; **Twelfth**: adjective from twelve; **Wisdom**: knowledge; **Zoology**: study of animals

UNIT 2

1 No
2 No
3 It's imaginative, and has a repeating form.
4 A verb
5 Keeping
6 Yes, they all seem to be little things in life that he enjoys.

UNIT 3

1 Three: Iona, Hamish and the narrator
2 Position, height and speed
3 No, because it's so light.
4 It jabs its beak at the gloves.
5 Migration
6 Because of the dialogue
7 It asks the questions you might want to ask, and makes it a more human account.

UNIT 4

1 Wild animals in wild places
2 She was a vet
3 Yes, she worked as a vet abroad
4 She must have studied to be a vet; and then later did a Masters Degree in Writing for Young People
5 Yes, she has 'a young family'
6 They must be very varied pets
7 In the third person
8 Ten times
9

Past	Present	Future
A	—	
	B	
C	C	
D		
E		
	F	
	G	

UNIT 5

1 sandals, trainers, wellingtons
2 For example, pumps, flip-flops, mules
3 shiny
4 The first group is about surprise; the second group is about offence.
5 For example, I bought some pills from the chemist.
6 **Aim** is where you intend to shoot; **shoot** is when you actually fire.

UNIT 7
Get ready

buy	bought
bring	brought
fight	fought
seek	sought
think	thought

Let's practise

off	oh	oo	ow	or	uh	uff
cough	dough	through	plough	nought	thorough	rough
trough	though		drought		borough	tough
	although					enough

Have a go

aught	eight
caught	freight
fraught	weight
daughter	sleight
haughty	height

UNIT 8
Get ready

Root verb	Add the suffix
change	changeable
comfort	comfortable
consider	considerable
depend	dependable
enjoy	enjoyable
notice	noticeable
reason	reasonable
understand	understandable
stop	stoppable
like	likable

Let's practise

Noun	Adjective
expectation	expectant
hesitation	hesitant
observation	observant
confidence	confident
independence	independent
obedience	obedient

Have a go
Dependent is an adjective;
dependant is a noun (like
assistant, for instance).

UNIT 9

1 The **principal** thing is to remember the **principle**.
2 I must **practise** how to do my **practice**.
3 My driving **licence license**s me to drive a car.
4 I'm not sure how that will **affect** me; there could be a big **effect**.
5 I **passed** by and then hurried on **past**.
6 My car is **stationary** while I buy some **stationery**.
7 Give me a **compliment**; it will **complement** the others I've received.
8 We stagger across the **desert** to reach a place that serves **dessert**.
9 We pray at the **altar**; hoping that will **alter** things for us.
10 Is it **allowed** to call **aloud**?

UNIT 10

1 **a** isle, **b** aisle
2 **a** father, **b** farther
3 **a** guest, **b** guessed
4 **a** herd, **b** heard
5 **a** cereal, **b** serial
6 **a** draught, **b** draft
7 **a** steel, **b** steal
8 **a** bridal, **b** bridle
9 **a** profit, **b** prophet
10 **a** mourning, **b** morning

UNIT 11
Get ready

1 The email was sent by him last week.
2 A reply was sent by her immediately.
3 Her attention was really caught by the message.
4 Another email was sent by him the next morning.
5 He was rung by her, to discuss it further.
6 His phone got dropped in his surprise.
7 Her friends were told all about it.
8 The message was passed on by them.
9 The question couldn't be answered by anybody.

Let's practise

1 The scientist studied the insect.
2 They also observed its diet for a week.
3 The newspaper recorded the scientist's results.
4 The newspaper's sales rose that week.
5 Nobody expected this.
6 Everybody praised the scientist.
7 Everybody forgot the insect soon after.

UNIT 14
Have a go

1 semicolon
2 colon
3 colon
4 semicolon

UNIT 18
Let's practise
Bird 1: Oh, wait, now what's she doing?

Bird 2: She's heading straight for the fence!

Bird 3: Podgy! The cat's on there, Podgy!

[*Voices off*] Podgy! Podgy! Not there, Podgy!

Bird 1: Cor, she's a proper liability, that pigeon!

Bird 2: She does my brain in!

Bird 3: Oh no, I can't believe it!

[*Voices off*] She's going for the bin and there's a cat behind it! PODGY!

Have a go
The three birds sat watching Podgy, as she dive-bombed the fence:

"Oh, wait, now what's she doing?"

"She's heading straight for the fence!"

"Podgy!" called the third. "The cat's on there, Podgy!"

"Podgy!" "Podgy!" "Not there, Podgy!" they chorused.

Then, as Podgy aimed for the dustbin, they started again:

"Cor, she's a proper liability, that pigeon!"

"She does my brain in!"

"Oh no, I can't believe it!"

"She's going for the bin and there's a cat behind it!" "PODGY!"

How have I done?
Comprehension
Poetry: verses, rhyme, metre

Fiction: narrative, setting, character, plot

Information: factual, different sub-genres

Reference: headwords, word class, definition, sample sentence

Handwriting
Print for labels

Joins for formal writing

For your own notes, a more informal style that you can still read yourself

Composition
The quick, brown fox was exhausted. "Not more jumping," he said.

"Well," said the lazy dog, "you don't want to lose your reputation, do you?"

"Oh well, just this time," the fox moaned, and changed into his trainers.

WRITING AND PUNCTUATION

UNIT 1
1 Five lines
2 8, 8, 5 or 6, 5 or 6, 8
3 1, 2, 5; 3, 4
4 Lines 1 and 5

UNIT 2
1 In italic in square brackets
2 Present tense
3 In capital letters
4 No
5 Usually the speech

UNIT 3
1 Speech marks
2 Inside the speech marks
3 To introduce each new speech
4 Asked, replied

UNIT 6
1 There was once . . .
2 So that each cub can behave in a different way
3 The lioness
4 'rather boring', 'fell into the river', 'hid behind a large cactus'
5 *Carefully does it. Fools rush in . . .*, etc.

UNIT 7
1 They probably existed, because of all the legends about them.
2 Probably not, as his behaviour was so magical.
3 Bravery and honour
4 Gawain was spared three times, for the three times he'd resisted the green knight's wife.

UNIT 8
Let's practise
Briefly, the Nurse is saying, "Don't mess her about!"

UNIT 10
1 First paragraph starts by describing the setting.
2 Second paragraph describes the plot.
3 'what a subtle writer he is and how carefully and poetically he uses language'; 'Almond makes familiar issues fresh; his characters are finely drawn and his depiction of place perfectly realised.'
4 Yes, the reviewer liked the book.

UNIT 11
1 Because it's a quote from the book
2 To involve you in how the plot might develop

UNIT 12
1 First paragraph involves the reader
2 Second paragraph promises a solution to the problem of rainy days
3 Third paragraph provides technical explanation
4 Fourth paragraph tells you where to get hold of the product

UNIT 13
1 Present tense
2 Probably a diagram would help

UNIT 14
1 What you need; What to do
2 Nouns; imperative verbs
3 List, capital letters, no full stops; sentences with capital letters and full stops

UNIT 15
1 The part of speech
2 The adjective
3 The verb 'shock'

UNIT 17
1 The extract is written in the first person.
2 Past tense
3 Early family life
4 When they sent a tape to the record company and someone came to hear them play.

UNIT 19
Against
Our climate is too hot for polar bears.
Animals should live in their natural habitat.
We can see animals on nature films.

For
Letting children see what polar bears look like

UNIT 20
1 A numbered list
2 'marks can be awarded', 'marks should be given', 'marks are then converted', 'tests are marked', 'results are sent'
3 Teachers, and possibly parents

How have I done?
Quiz on writing
Any correct answer

Quiz on punctuation
1 The king, who was very old, could not kneel down in his tight breeches.
2 He asked the queen, "Could you help me, please?"
3 "Not on your life," she said.
4 "I have it in mind to steal the throne, if you're not up to it."
5 So, without a pause, she vaulted over the poor man and plonked herself on the throne.
6 The courtiers cried out, "What's all this?"
7 They held a quick referendum (or quiz). Would people prefer a king or a queen?
8 The result of the vote was six for the king and four for the queen.
9 So in the end the king got himself back on the throne, in the nick of time *or* So, in the end, the king got himself back on the throne, in the nick of time.
10 "Never mind," he said to the queen. "Better luck next time!"

MATHS

UNIT 1

1 Fifty three thousand one hundred and thirty two
2 Seventeen thousand three hundred and thirty three
3 Three hundred and seventy thousand three hundred and eleven
4 One hundred thousand and six
5 Five hundred and five thousand and fifty
6 Six hundred and nine thousand and nine
7 Seven hundred and sixty three thousand two hundred and seven
8 Six hundred thousand
9 Eighty
10 Thirty thousand
11 Six thousand
12 Two hundred thousand
13 Six hundred
14 378848   379848   380848
    502592   512592   522592   532592
    308992   309012   309022   309032

UNIT 2

1 34390
2 83350
3 25320
4 275170
5 194200
6 174210
7 37300
8 710300
9 376900
10 363500
11 274480   193260   375990
    274500   193300   376000
    274000   193000   376000
    270000   190000   380000
    300000   200000   400000
12 550
13 1149
14 4500
15 94999

UNIT 3

1 3, 6, 9, 12, 15, 18, 21, 24, 27, 30, 33, 36
2 6, 12, 18, 24, 30, 36, 42, 48, 54, 60, 66, 72
3 4, 8, 12, 16, 20, 24, 28, 32, 36, 40, 44, 48
4 6, 12, 18, 24, 30, 36
5 12, 24, 36
6 12
7 6
8 10
9 30
10 15
11 20
12 21
13 56
14 28
15 30
16 20
17 24

UNIT 4

1 True
2 False
3 True
4 True
5 False
6 True
7 False
8 True
9 True
10 1, 2, 3, 5, 7, 11, 13, 17, 19, 23, 29, 31, 37, 41, 43, 47, 53, 59, 61, 67, 71, 73, 79, 83, 89, 97
11 They are prime numbers

UNIT 5

1 38 977
2 33 362
3 81 081
4 86 788
5 106 138
6 112 227
7 59 090
8 88 256
9 68 860
10 61 891
11 91 121
12 131 300

UNIT 6

1 27 233
2 20 297
3 17 449
4 18 757
5 15 769
6 35 182
7 23 078
8 43 648
9 18 875
10 24 916
11 26 839
12 36 265

UNIT 7

1

×	1	2	3	4	5	6	7	8	9	10	11	12
1	1	2	3	4	5	6	7	8	9	10	11	12
2	2	4	6	8	10	12	14	16	18	20	22	24
3	3	6	9	12	15	18	21	24	27	30	33	36
4	4	8	12	16	20	24	28	32	36	40	44	48
5	5	10	15	20	25	30	35	40	45	50	55	60
6	6	12	18	24	30	36	42	48	54	60	66	72
7	7	14	21	28	35	42	49	56	63	70	77	84
8	8	16	24	32	40	48	56	64	72	80	88	96
9	9	18	27	36	45	54	63	72	81	90	99	108
10	10	20	30	40	50	60	70	80	90	100	110	120
11	11	22	33	44	55	66	77	88	99	110	121	132
12	12	24	36	48	60	72	84	96	108	120	132	144

2

84	49	72
84	44	64
36	144	81
60	88	132
56	0	6
99	120	0
108	35	42
90	24	30
32	108	48
33	60	96
63	66	121

UNIT 8

1 3 730
2 8 600
3 68 000
4 67 300
5 2 400
6 930
7 42
8 8 440
9 19
10 8 650
11 2 100
12 480
13 48 000
14 66 000
15 10 800
16 4 200
17 14 000
18 25 000
19 56 000
20 84 000

UNIT 9

1 1 836
2 8 100
3 13 712
4 147 906
5 432 718
6 3 480
7 £67 644

UNIT 10

1 297
2 71r1
3 31r3
4 51r4
5 56r1
6 27r6
7 59
8 98
9 74r1
10 94
11 66
12 269r1
13 $77\frac{1}{2}$
14 $14\frac{1}{4}$
15 $53\frac{1}{4}$
16 $313\frac{1}{2}$
17 $60\frac{3}{4}$
18 $43\frac{3}{4}$
19 347
20 357
21 945
22 235
23 247
24 736
25 135

UNIT 11

1 $\frac{2}{5}$

2 $\frac{5}{6}$

3 $\frac{7}{8}$

4 $\frac{1}{3}$

5 $\frac{10}{12}$

6 $\frac{1}{2}$

7 $\frac{3}{12}$　　$\frac{4}{12}$

　　$\frac{6}{12}$　　$\frac{10}{12}$

　　$\frac{9}{12}$　　$\frac{8}{12}$

8 $\frac{1}{2}$　$\frac{11}{20}$　$\frac{7}{10}$　$\frac{3}{4}$　$\frac{4}{5}$

UNIT 12

1

2

3 $\frac{5}{4}$

4 $\frac{7}{4}$

5 $\frac{10}{4}$

6 $\frac{13}{4}$

7 $\frac{17}{4}$

8 $\frac{15}{4}$

9 $2\frac{1}{4}$

10 $1\frac{1}{2}$

11 $2\frac{3}{4}$

12 $4\frac{1}{2}$

13 $3\frac{1}{4}$

14 $4\frac{3}{4}$

UNIT 13

1 0.7

2 0.09

3 0.17

4 0.8

5 0.06

6 0.15

7 0.57

8 0.61

9 $\frac{8}{10}$

10 $\frac{7}{100}$

11 $1\frac{2}{10}$

12 $\frac{27}{100}$

13 $\frac{48}{100}$

14 $6\frac{4}{10}$

15 $\frac{5}{100}$

16 $\frac{99}{100}$

17 $\frac{5}{10}$　　$\frac{1}{2}$

18 $\frac{5}{100}$　　$\frac{1}{20}$

19 $\frac{6}{10}$　　$\frac{3}{5}$

20 $\frac{25}{100}$　　$\frac{1}{4}$

21 $\frac{75}{100}$　　$\frac{3}{4}$

22 $\frac{4}{100}$　　$\frac{1}{25}$

UNIT 14

1 4%

2 9%

3 16%

4 80%

5 6%

6 15%

7 57%

8 61%

9 $\frac{80}{100}$　　80%

10 $\frac{7}{100}$　　7%

11	$\frac{20}{100}$	20%
12	$\frac{27}{100}$	27%
13	$\frac{48}{100}$	48%
14	$\frac{40}{100}$	40%
15	$\frac{5}{100}$	5%
16	$\frac{99}{100}$	99%
17	$\frac{50}{100}$	$\frac{1}{2}$
18	$\frac{25}{100}$	$\frac{1}{4}$
19	$\frac{75}{100}$	$\frac{3}{4}$
20	$\frac{20}{100}$	$\frac{1}{5}$
21	$\frac{5}{100}$	$\frac{1}{20}$
22	$\frac{4}{100}$	$\frac{1}{25}$

UNIT 15

1 Isosceles
2 Scalene
3 Isosceles
4 Scalene
5 Isosceles
6 Equilateral
7

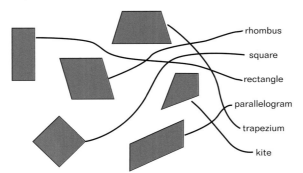

rhombus
square
rectangle
parallelogram
trapezium
kite

UNIT 16

1 Obtuse
2 Reflex
3 Acute
4 Obtuse
5 Reflex
6 Right
7 300°
8 210°
9 275°
10 235°

UNIT 17

1 8
2 1 500
3 2.5
4 10 000
5 15 000
6 15
7 28 000
8 41
9 10
10 9 500
11 30
12 15
13 45
14 63
15 60
16 2
17 12
18 2

UNIT 18

1 $6\,\text{cm}^2$
2 $8\,\text{cm}^2$
3 $9\,\text{cm}^2$
4 $15\,\text{cm}^2$
5 $5\,\text{cm}^2$
6 $7\,\text{cm}^2$
7 10 cm   16 cm
   12 cm   12 cm
   12 cm   16 cm
8 $28\,\text{cm}^2$ $48\,\text{cm}^2$
   $30\,\text{cm}^2$ $36\,\text{cm}^2$
9 22 cm   28 cm
   22 cm   26 cm

UNIT 19

1 $\frac{1}{4}$

2 $\frac{1}{6}$

3 $\frac{7}{12}$

4 3

5 2

6 7

7 $\frac{1}{6}$

8 $\frac{1}{3}$

9 $\frac{1}{2}$

10 4

11 8

12 12

13 Won 6   draws 1   lost 5

How have I done?

1 four hundred and thirty-three thousand, five hundred and sixty-eight
2 493 373, 503 373
3 53 550
4 63 600
5 57 000
6 30
7 11, 2, 7, 23, 31
8 55 077, 23 682, 72 400
   84 381, 46 653, 506
9 56, 132, 64,
   7, 12, 6 r 1
10 15 300
11 433 r 3 or 433.75 or $433\frac{3}{4}$
12 $\frac{11}{24}$, $\frac{1}{2}$, $\frac{7}{12}$, $\frac{3}{4}$, $\frac{5}{6}$
13 3 ¼
14 0.75 and ¾
15 isosceles
16 $200°$
17 $40\,\text{cm}^2$, 26 cm

PROBLEM SOLVING

UNIT 1
1. Nine hundred and seventy-five
2. Two hundred and forty-five
3. Nine hundred and ninety-seven
4. Eight hundred and sixty-one
5. 3478
6. 8753
7. 1246
8. 9875
9. $93 \times 75 + 1 = 6976$

UNIT 2
1. 256 miles
2. $\frac{4}{24} = \frac{1}{6}$
3. 5 minutes
4. 35
5. £42
6. 40 minutes
7. 280
8. £21

Have a go: $\frac{1}{3}$

UNIT 3
1. 9.05 m
2. 10.85 m
3. 22 seconds
4. 49.3 seconds
5. Jamelia, by 2.62 m
6. 39.3 seconds
7. 2.24 cm
8. The children, by 53.73 kg

UNIT 4
1. £81
2. £30.50
3. £10
4. £60
5. £211.60
6. £333.50
7. £19.25
8. £65

Have a go: £10.92

UNIT 5
1. 761
2. 1409
3. 1871
4. 4041
5. 13 322
6. 15 969
7. 12 557
8. 7716
9. 30 877 (Don't count Charlie and Abbie!)

UNIT 6
(Answers relevant to 2007)
1. 89 years
2. 117 years
3. 170 years
4. 251 years
5. 341 years
6. 251 years
7. 461 years
8. 1005 years
9. 4600 years

UNIT 7
1. 296
2. 405
3. £21.25
4. £25.65
5. £41.76
6. 1296
7. 8648
8. £103.60

UNIT 8
1. 24
2. 29
3. $432 \div 12 = 36$, $432 \div 8 = 54$. A club would receive 18 tickets more than school.
4. 4 hours 20 minutes
5. £80
6. £45
7. 2250
8. 16 800
9. £25

Have a go: 5625

UNIT 9

1 £180
2 £117
3 £155
4 £145.01
5 20 weeks
6 £134.60
7 £15.27
8 £119.33
9 £140

UNIT 10

1 1 hour 25 minutes
2 1.40 p.m.
3 4.35 p.m.
4 $8\frac{1}{2}$ hours
5 Chicken: 1 hour, 1 hour 20 min, 1 hour 40 min, 2 hours, 2 hours 20 min, 2 hours 40 min
6 Nut roast: 1 hour 15 min, 1 hour 40 min, 2 hours 5 min, 2 hours 30 min, 2 hours 55 min, 3 hours 20 min
7 Pork: 1 hour 25 min, 1 hour 55 min, 2 hours 25 min, 2 hours 55 min, 3 hours 25 min, 3 hours 55 min
8 Frozen vegetable lasagne: 1 hour 50 min, 2 hours 30 min, 3 hours 10 min, 3 hours 50 min, 4 hours 30 min, 5 hours 10 min
9 2.02 p.m.

UNIT 11

1 936 g
2 95.5 m
3 90 m
4 6100 cm
5 21.5 m
6 275 ml
7 60 sausages, weighing 600 g
8 21.45 kg
9 12.08 l

UNIT 12

1 160
2 9 and 1
3 32 and 23; or 41 and 14
4 20
5 3 pairs
6 122 and 123
7 120
8 301
9 96 coins: 32 × 50p, 32 × 20p, 32 × 10p

UNIT 13

1 Moscow 1980, Los Angeles 1984
2 London 1948, Rome 1960
3 2016, 2020, 2024
4 25
5 No, because it only appears every 76 years.
6 1142, 1218 and 1294
7 13
8 2262 and 2397
9 15
Have a go: 51 World Cups

UNIT 14

1 Isosceles triangle
2 Hexagon
3 Irregular pentagon
4 Rhombus
5 12
6 Trapezium
7 Equilateral triangle and parallelogram (or an irregular hexagon)
8 Four, three and six
9 24

UNIT 15

1 4
2 3
3 7
4 3
5 Pink
6 Green
7 False
8 12
9 14
10 20

UNIT 16

1 Wet 'n' Wild!
2 (−2, −3)
3 (−6, −5)
4 Sandpit
5 Penguins
6 (−6, 1)
7 Vertical Splash!
8 (2, 4)
9 No, the Queasy Rider is at (3, −4)
10 (−5, −6), (−5, 6), (5, 6), (5, −6)

UNIT 17

1 5
2 Crashing his monkey scooter
3 6
4 20
5 1 to 10
6 11 to 20
7 20
8 44
9 68

How have I done?

1 9824
2 300
3 38.9 cm
4 £52
5 10 405
6 186 years
7 £66.75
8 18
9 £15.10
10 82 minutes
11 21.15 km
12 167 or 149
13 2003
14 Scalene triangle
15 Hemisphere or cone
16 West